Selena Ibbott

AN ENGLISH ROSE

Traditional
Beauty Recipes
for Creams,
Essences, Perfumes
and Tonics

Illustrations by
Margaret Whiting

ASHGROVE PRESS, BATH

First published in Great Britain by
ASHGROVE PRESS LIMITED
4 Brassmill Centre, Brassmill Lane
Bath BA1 3JN
and distributed in the USA by
Avery Publishing Group Inc.
120 Old Broadway
Garden City Park
New York 11040

First published 1990

British Library Cataloguing in Publication Data
Ibbott, Selena
An English Rose
1. Women. Beauty care. Use of natural products. Manuals
1. Title
646.7'2
ISBN 1–85398–007–2

Photoset by Ann Buchan, Middlesex
Printed and bound in Great Britain
by Dotesios Printers Ltd, Trowbridge, Wiltshire

Dedication

This book is lovingly dedicated to my mother
who shared with me both her love and
knowledge of herbs and guided me through the
pages of this book.

Acknowledgements

Without the help, support, and 'wisdom' of my family this book would have been impossible to write. I would like to thank my grandmothers Violet Upham and Jessie Pearce, my great grandmothers Louisa Thompkins and Florence Durrant and their mothers, Sarah Abrahams and Martha Page, who passed down through the generations endless remedies, superstitions and information which inspired and led me to compile this book.

I'd also like to thank Rosemary Williams who through her blindness taught me many things as a child, one of them being that the ugliest jagged piece of rock holds within itself a rare beauty of its own; my dear friend Gillian Entwistle, self-employed hairdresser, for enthusiasm and advice on hair and skin; and Robin Campbell, whose faith in me made it all possible!

Contents

1 *Introduction*

This book is for natural beauty lovers, to be read, used and enjoyed. It is full of useful tips and cures, both old and new. It contains over 150 remedies, many of which have been handed down to me from my grandmother, mother and wise old great aunts. Some date back to the 16th Century, a few date back even further.

While researching for this book, I found myself constantly referring back to a book that was given to me by my grandmother. It has no date of publication, but as my grandmother can recall it always being on the shelf when she was a child, it must be early 19th Century, possibly older. Again and again I dipped into it with fascination and delight, each time discovering something new. I came across many ancient remedies which I had regretfully to exclude, as the ingredients are no longer available, one of which was an anti-wrinkle cream: the main ingredient was fresh whale sperm, together with freshly skinned hare flesh, to be eaten raw daily.

Measurements were a problem, as many things were measured in 'bushels', 'scruples', 'drams' and 'grains.' But with time and patience, trial and error, I managed to convert to pounds, ounces, tablespoons and teaspoons.

Ingredients.   Most of the herbs that you will need for the remedies can be obtained from good health shops or herbal stores, already dried and sealed in jars. It is a lot cheaper to buy dried herbs loose. Many health food shops have a wide selection.

It is important to keep herbs carefully labelled, in airtight stopper-jars, to prevent them from going musty.

To collect and dry your own herbs, see *Drying and Storing Herbs*, p. 137. Once you have discovered your favourite herbs, those that you always want to keep in stock, you will be surprised how quickly your ingredients will build up.

For the oils and essences that are vital when it comes to making bath oils and perfumes, try the chemist or your old-fashioned corner shop, before you try the more expensive herbal stores. It is best not to stock up with oils, as they will evaporate if not used within a few months.

Equipment.   You will find many things in the kitchen, but you will need to buy some additional bits and pieces.

A pestle and mortar is vital.

A yard of butter-muslin or cotton, which is very reasonable to buy, will last over a month, depending on how much you use, to make bath bags, lavender bags and scented sachets.

You will need a sieve for straining: an ordinary nylon sieve will do. At times you may need a very fine sieve, which I line with muslin.

A good stock of glass screw-topped jars and plastic containers is essential for storing the herbs. Keep fancy bottles and plastic containers of all kinds, different pots and jars, empty shampoo bottles, anything that will come in handy to fill with your own home-made beauty products.

Odd pieces of material, scraps of ribbon and lace will come in handy to make attractive sachets, bags, and sleep pillows: gifts that you will want to keep.

* * *

It has been both a joy and a pleasure compiling this book. It has been interesting and fun, researching through old books and taking note of old wives' tales and superstitions, and collecting and making remedies that were passed down to me.

I hope that you will have as much enjoyment reading this book as I had writing it.

Selena Ibbott

2 *Recipes for Natural Beauty*

SKIN

Naturally beautiful, clear, soft skin is largely hereditary; but even a woman who has been blessed with a beautiful, perfectly balanced, evenly coloured complexion – which is rare – will need to pay it constant care and attention, with correctly formulated products, to keep it supple and young-looking. But with time, care and proper attention, cleansing thoroughly and moisturising regularly, you can help to keep your skin looking its best, whatever type of skin you have.

Adding herbs to cosmetics provides a natural way of caring for your skin. It is fun and interesting to make your own bath oils, creams and perfumes, and, unlike shop-bought cosmetics, they cost remarkably little. The remedies in this section will not bring miracles, but you will find that natural, home-made remedies work just as well as expensive, bought products.

So treat your skin the natural way, for natural beauty.

* * *

Hard water with too strong a soap is ruinous to the

complexion, and soap should never be used with cold water. Whether you use soap or cream, always cleanse your face thoroughly before going to bed, particularly if you wear foundation throughout the day. Remove all trace of make-up, as it will encourage blackheads and enlarged pores.

Remember that a clear complexion is not made by external applications alone: no amount of make-up will improve the skin if it has been neglected. Creams, moisturisers and lotions will help, but for a clear skin drink water daily before meals, as water renews the tissues and will help to clear the skin of pimples and blotches. Sleep is also necessary for a clear skin, together with a healthy diet, fresh air and exercise.

Keeping the skin soft and supple is very important. If the skin is neglected and allowed to become dry, tiny flakes of dead skin will build up on the surface and clog up open, large pores, causing blackheads, spots and blemishes.

To prevent dead skin cells flaking and building up on the skin, cleanse thoroughly and slough off any dead skin with fine oatmeal mixed to a paste with warm water. Rub into the skin and allow to dry, rinse off with warm water, then splash the face with cold water to close any enlarged pores. Moisturise the face well with a rich cream moisturiser, massaging into the face with firm upward strokes using the fingertips.

Know Your Skin Type

For the best results when looking after your skin you need to know your skin type, which will help you to choose products that will keep it in good condition.

Examine your face in a mirror and identify your skin type, using the descriptions below.

COMBINATION SKIN
Combination skin is a mixture of oily and dry skin. Usually the areas around the neck, cheeks and eyes are dry, and the forehead, chin and nose oily. When using make-up, you might find that the oily parts of the face are shiny, spoiling the make-up.

If this is the case, then it is best to use two different moisturisers: one for the dry areas, and another for the oily parts. For the oily parts, use a specifically formulated moisturiser.

DRY SKIN
Dry skin feels taut after washing. It also has a tendency to small broken veins and patches of flakiness, and is prone to blemish. It wrinkles easily, and ages more quickly than other skin types.

Dry skin needs constant attention. Use mild and gentle, soothing formulations that maintain and enrich moisture levels. It needs to be well protected from the sun. During hot weather, keep the skin oiled regularly with olive oil, or rosewater and glycerine.

NORMAL SKIN
True 'normal' skin is rare, so if you have been blessed with this skin type you are extremely lucky. However, to keep it looking well balanced, evenly coloured and textured and clear, it will still need time and care: regular cleansing and massaging, protection from heat, fog, and dust, and

applying a correctly formulated cream and moisturiser will keep it at its best.

OILY SKIN

Oily skin is due to over-active sebaceous glands. It is coarse in texture and, unlike dry skin, is not prone to wrinkle, but suffers instead from spots and blackheads, especially around the chin. It will blemish easily, and also becomes shiny around the nose and chin, even through make-up, unless a product is chosen with care.

SENSITIVE SKIN

Sensitive skin tends to be dry, but can also be greasy. It will react immediately to change in temperature, and sometimes to different foods. It has a tendency to broken veins, reddish patches, and is also prone to spots. It will react to some cosmetics, and certain skin creams.

Take care in choosing a formulated product for sensitive skin.

'Beauty is not only fair of face, real beauty lies within.'

Creams and Lotions for the Face

COCOA BUTTER FACE CREAM

When massaged into the skin, this slightly scented cream will unblock large pores and purify the skin, leaving your skin soft and smooth.

3 tablespoons cocoa butter	2 ½ tablespoons sweet
1 tablespoon lanolin	almond oil
	60 drops simple tincture of benzoin

Melt the cocoa butter together with the lanolin in an earthenware jug standing in a pan of boiling water.

Add the sweet almond oil and beat well. While beating add the simple tinture of benzoin a few drops at a time. Beat to a cream.

Store in a small glass pot or jar.

This cream is a little hard, until it comes in contact with the skin, when it will immediately melt.

CUCUMBER FACE CREAM

This cream is pleasant to use, gentle and kind to the face.

| 2 cucumbers | 1 ½ tablespoons lanolin |
| 6 tablespoons olive oil | 3 tablespoons white wax |

Wash the cucumbers and slice about an inch thick with the peel on.

Soak them in the olive oil for 24 hours.

Press to a pulp in the olive oil, then strain through a sieve.

Melt together the white wax and the lanolin, and add to the cucumber pulp. Beat to a cream.

Store in a glass pot, or a handy plastic container.

I don't think that this cream needs any perfume, but a few drops of oil of violets will slightly scent it if you prefer.

HONEY FACE CREAM

Honey and glycerine are two of the oldest moisturizers known. This cream will prevent wrinkles. It is pleasant to use, even if a bit sticky.

2 tablespoons clear honey
1 tablespoon rosewater
1 tablespoon witch hazel
1 tablespoon glycerine

Mix all the ingredients together and stir thoroughly.
Store in a screw-topped jar.
Apply to the face and neck, morning and night.

ROSE CLEANSING CREAM

To make this simple inexpensive cleansing cream all you will need is

¼ lb lard
2 tablespoons rosewater

Put the lard into a basin, and pour over enough boiling water to fill the basin. Leave until the water becomes cold, and the lard floats on top. Pour off the water, and repeat the process until the lard has been melted three times.
Put the lard into a clean basin, and add the rosewater. Beat to a cream.
Store in a pot or screw-topped jar in a warm place.
Use to cleanse the face. This is a good cream for an oily skin: it will unblock large pores as well as soften the skin.

GLYCERINE SKIN LOTION

4 tablespoons glycerine   ½ pint camphor water
2 tablespoons powdered
  borax

Dissolve the powdered borax in the camphor water.

Pour the liquid into a glass bottle, add the glycerine and shake well.

To use: On a clean face last thing at night, apply to the skin with a pad of cotton wool; or under make-up during the day, apply to the skin, and when the lotion is dry, dust over the face with a little face powder. This will help to disguise red blotches on the skin, and prevent freckles.

For lotions to remove and fade freckles, see *Freckles*, p. 25.

OATMEAL CLEANSING LOTION

To cleanse and soften the face and throat.

½ pint rosewater   1 tablespoon fine oatmeal
1 teaspoon simple tincture
  benzoin

Pour the rosewater into a glass bottle with a wide mouth.

Add the simple tincture of benzoin a drop at a time, shaking as you do so.

Sieve the oatmeal before adding to the liquid. Shake well.

Creams and Lotions for the Body

CUCUMBER BODY CREAM

This body cream is both light and refreshing. Use it all over the body, for all-over freshness, especially in hot weather. It is so mild and gentle, you can also use it on your face.

3 fresh cucumbers
12 tablespoons oil of sweet
    almonds
lanolin

white wax
1 teaspoon simple
    tincture of benzoin

Wash and peel the cucumbers, and slice about an inch thick.
Place in a jar, and pour the sweet almond oil over them.
Put the jar into a pan of boiling water and simmer for 5 to 6 hours.
Strain through a sieve lined with muslin and measure.
To each 6 oz of liquid, add 2 oz of lanolin and 1 oz of white wax.
Heat again, until the lanolin and the wax have melted into the cucumber. Stir thoroughly, then remove from heat and beat to a cream, adding the teaspoon of simple tincture of benzoin while beating.
Store in a handy plastic container.
Use daily, for refreshing smooth skin.

ORANGE BODY CREAM

2 tablespoons orange water
1 teaspoon oil of orange

4 tablespoons oil of sweet
  almonds
8 tablespoons white wax

Put the wax into an earthenware jug, and stand it in a pan of boiling water to melt.

Once melted, remove from heat and add the orange water and the oil of orange. Beat in well. While beating, add the oil of sweet almonds. Beat to a cream.

Store in a container or jar. Use all over the body to soften and scent the skin.

MILK OF ALMONDS SKIN LOTION

This lotion will cleanse, soften and lighten the skin. Use on the face, body and hands.

60 almonds
½ pint distilled water

1 tablespoon white sugar

Put the almonds into a mortar and bruise.

Add the water and beat together, adding the tablespoon of sugar to prevent the oil separating from the water.

Bottle.

Apply to the skin with a pad of cotton wool.

CUCUMBER BODY LOTION

This lovely, light green, fresh-smelling lotion rubs in easily and leaves your skin smooth and scented. It is very refreshing to use in hot weather after a bath.

1 fresh cucumber	1 tablespoon rosewater
1 tablespoon witch hazel	1 teaspoon glycerine

Wash and peel the cucumber and cut into pieces about 2 inches thick.
Either: mash the cucumber and add the witch hazel, rosewater and glycerine, and beat well.
Or: use a blender: put all the ingredients in together, and blend for about 30 seconds.
Store in a plastic container and use when required.

LAVENDER BODY LOTION

1 cup lavender: flowers, tops, leaves and stalks	1 teaspoon borax
2 cups boiling water	a few drops oil of lavender
2 tablespoons ground nut oil	

Put the lavender into an earthenware jug and pour over the boiling water. Cover the jug with a plate or saucer, and leave to steep overnight or for 8 hours.
Dissolve the borax in the lavender infusion before straining.

Warm the ground nut oil and add to the lavender infusion, beating well. An electric mixer or hand whisk is a great help.

Add a few drops of the lavender oil and bottle, shaking well to blend in the oil.

Shake well before using. This is a good lotion to use all over the body after a relaxing herbal bath. It will leave your skin soft, smooth and fragrant.

VIOLET BODY LOTION

This lotion is sweet-smelling and soothing. It is refreshing to use after a bath for all-over freshness. It will soften, scent and refine the skin, and as it is so mild and gentle, it can be used as a face freshener.

1 handful violet flowers, freshly picked or dried	½ pint fresh milk

Put the violet flowers into a china bowl or an earthenware jug.

Gently warm the milk, and then pour it over the violet flowers. Cover the container with a plate or saucer, and leave for 3 hours.

Strain through a sieve lined with muslin and bottle. Keep this lotion in the fridge. It will keep fresh for 1 week.

Shake well before using.

Apply to the skin with a pad of cotton wool. This is one of my favourite lotions, especially when used after a herbal bath that has been scented with violet bath oil (see p. 96).

Face Packs

Face packs or 'masks' are an important part of beauty treatment. A face pack will cleanse the skin; when used regularly it will gradually fade wrinkles. It will also unblock large pores, tone up sagging muscles, and may be used as a semi-bleaching agent. Whether you have an oily, dry and blotchy or combination skin, I'm sure that you will find a face pack here to suit your skin type. I recommend the grape juice pack: it is cool, light and very refreshing, especially during hot weather.

CREAM FACE PACK

For all skin types.
Cut a round piece of butter-muslin about the same size as your face, and cut holes for the eyes, nostrils and mouth. Put the muslin to soak in a bowl of fresh dairy cream.
Cleanse the face thoroughly, splash over with warm water, then pat dry with a warm towel.
Place the muslin over the face, pressing it firmly onto the skin. Leave it on for 20 minutes.
Remove by dabbing the face with a warm towel that has been squeezed out in warm water.

EGG FACE PACK

For dry skin. This egg pack will draw all the impurities out of the skin, leaving your face soft and smooth.

yolks of 2 large fresh eggs   20 drops simple tincture
                                 of benzoin

Beat together the egg yolks, adding the simple tincture of benzoin a drop at a time while beating.
Paint the mixture over the face thickly, and allow to dry on the face.
Leave on the face for 20 minutes, or longer if necessary. It must be perfectly dry before removing with warm water.

GRAPE JUICE FACE PACK

For all skin types. This pack lightens the skin, and is also very refreshing. All you will need is

1 small bunch white
   seedless grapes

Mash the grapes to a pulp and pass them through a sieve.
Cleanse the face, then spread the grape pulp over the face.
Leave for 20 minutes, then rinse off.
Splash the face with a little cold water to close the pores, and pat dry with a warm towel.

HONEY FACE PACK

For all skin types.

whites of 3 large fresh eggs
2 tablespoons honey

1½ tablespoons oil of
sweet almonds

Beat all the ingredients stiffly together, using a hand whisk.
To use: first wash the face with a little warm milk and water and pat dry with a warm towel.
Apply the mixture to the face: don't rub into the skin, merely spread over the face thickly and leave for 15 minutes.
Wash off with a little fine oatmeal in warm water.
Splash the face with cold water, to close any enlarged pores.
This is very good for the skin. It is sweet smelling and easy to apply, even if a bit sticky.

LEMON FACE PACK

For combination skin.

1 cup lemon verbena leaves
(dried or fresh)
1 carton natural yogurt

1 tablespoon fresh rain
water
1 tablespoon oatmeal

Simmer the lemon verbena leaves in the rain water for 5 minutes.
Strain through a sieve and bottle.

When the liquid is cool, add to the yogurt and oatmeal to form a paste.

Spread the mixture over the face, avoiding the areas around the mouth and eyes.

Leave for 20 minutes, then wash off with warm water.

MUD FACE PACK

For oily skin.

1 packet fuller's earth	½ teaspoon witch hazel
15 drops simple tincture of benzoin	½ teaspoon spirits of camphor

Add warm water to the earth and mix to a paste. Keep back a few handfuls of the earth, so that if the paste is too thin, you can thicken it.

Add the witch hazel, spirits of camphor and tincture of benzoin.

Apply to the face and neck with a brush.

When the mud has dried onto the face, leave for an extra 20 minutes.

Wash off with warm clear water.

OIL FACE PACK

For dry skin. This is excellent for removing wrinkles.

1 tablespoon oil of sweet almonds	10 drops simple tincture of Benzoin

First cut a piece of lint to cover the face and cut holes for the eyes, nostrils and mouth.

Add the oil of sweet almonds to the tincture of benzoin.

Apply the oil to the skin with a soft brush.

Lay the lint over the oiled face, and gently press onto the skin.

Leave for 10 to 15 minutes, then remove the oil with cotton wool soaked in warm water.

Before applying the oil to the skin, it is best to warm it slightly, in a jar standing in a pan of hot water.

YARROW FACE PACK

This pack is excellent for oily skin. It will open pores and cleanse thoroughly and deeply, preventing spots and blackheads. I can recommend this one as it is the one I use myself. Use once a week for a clear skin.

1 small cup of yarrow leaves (dried or fresh)	2 cups fresh rain water
1 carton natural yogurt	1 tablespoon fine oatmeal

Simmer the yarrow leaves in enough rain water to cover the leaves for 8 to 10 minutes, then strain.

When the yarrow infusion is cold, add to the yogurt and fine oatmeal, to form a paste.

To use: spread over the face, avoiding the areas around the eyes and mouth.

Leave for 10 minutes, then wash off with warm water and pat dry with a warm towel.

Mud Magic

Mud baths, face packs and shampoos may sound off-putting, but mud is one of the oldest beauty treatments, and it really works.

Earth and clay have been used for centuries. The first face packs were made from mud and clay, and women were using fuller's earth for beauty remedies long before cosmetic companies produced their own fancy versions. Mud has wonderful absorbent qualities that are perfect for drawing out impurities from the skin.

In certain parts of the world, mysterious healing muds have been found. Kaolin mud, which is a greyish-white colour, is served with morphine to relieve gastric problems; Rhassoul mud, which comes from the Atlas Mountains in Morocco, is excellent for cleansing the skin, and also has antiseptic qualities. Neydharting Moor mud, which is found in Austria, will help a weeping willow tree to flower, and change its colour each year. An ancient corpse was recently found perfectly preserved in the moor mud. This mud has been used to heal skin conditions, and to ease the pain in arthritis. You can even clean your teeth with moor mud. It will freshen the breath, and is used to treat gum disease and mouth ulcers, and as a mouth-wash. It consists of 80% mud and 20% essential oils, making it excellent for dry hair and skin.

There are many beauty muds available: ready-made face packs, shampoos and creams, but they are all very expensive. Making your own mud remedies is far cheaper, and they will work just as well.

You can buy kaolin from most Boots stores, but if you have trouble in getting either fuller's earth or kaolin, ask your chemist to order it for you.

Do not use any of the remedies in this next section if you suffer from high blood pressure.

MUD BUST MASK

Clay or mud makes a good base for a bust mask. The hardening action draws out the impurities and will tone, cleanse and lift your breasts. Use this mask once a week to deeply cleanse the pores, and for a clear smooth skin.

1 cup of kaolin powder   70 cm strip muslin
½ cup witch hazel

Put the kaolin into a small bowl.
Heat the witch hazel until nearly boiling, then add the witch hazel to the kaolin powder and mix together to form a paste.
Paint all the mixture thickly onto the muslin.
Place the covered muslin over the breasts and press on firmly.
Leave on until the mixture becomes cold.
Remove the muslin.
Rinse the breasts with warm water several times, then splash yourself three times with cold water.
Finish by applying body lotion while the skin is still damp, then pat dry with a warm towel.

MUD CLEANSER

This is a good cleanser as it will open and unblock enlarged pores, and soften the skin. It is excellent for normal skin types.

1 tablespoon fuller's earth	1 bottle rosewater and glycerine (200 ml; available from Boots)

Put the earth into a bowl and add the rosewater and glycerine.
Mix until the mixture is smooth and firm.
Apply to the face with a paint brush. The face should be thoroughly clean before applying.
Leave on for 5 minutes, then rinse off with warm water and splash the face with a little cold water to close the pores.

MUD BATH

There is no better way to cleanse the body than to take a mud bath. This may sound messy, but it is very relaxing. Mud has a three-way action: cleansing, toning and moisturising: an all-over body treatment that will leave your skin feeling soft and your muscles relaxed.

8–10 oz (according to body size) mud	water
1 packet fuller's earth powder	1 mugful fresh orange juice

Dig up a bucketful of garden earth. Remove any stones and lumps, and sieve until the earth is fine like peat. Measure out 8 oz (16 tablespoons) or 10 oz (20 tablespoons) and put into a large basin or clean bucket.

Add 6 tablespoons of fuller's earth powder and mix together.

Add the fresh orange juice to ½ pint hot water, and slowly pour the liquid into the earth, stirring thoroughly all the time. If the mixture is still stiff after adding the liquid, add more hot water; if too runny, add more earth. It should be like a paste, smooth and easy to apply to the body.

Using a clean paintbrush, paint your body all over with the mixture. Ask a friend to paint your back!

Stand in an empty bath for 10 minutes. Shower off with a strong warm shower, then rinse the body with cold water to finish, if you can bear it. Do not rub yourself dry afterwards. Wrap yourself in a warm bath robe or long towel, to dry the skin naturally. Once dry, massage the body all over with a good body lotion.

MUD FOR THE FACE

This is where the absorbent qualities of mud really come into play. It will draw out the skin's impurities, bringing spots and blackheads to the surface. It will cleanse the pores, and soften and nourish the skin.

MUD PACK FOR DRY SKIN

1 tablespoon fuller's earth	2 egg yolks
2 teaspoons sweet almond oil	

Mix all the ingredients together to form a paste.

Apply to the face with a paint brush. Apply generously, using all the mixture.

Leave on the face for no more than 5 minutes, so it doesn't have time to set hard.

Wash off with warm water, then splash the face with cold water, pat dry.

Apply a cleansing cream: use as normal, then moisturise the skin well.

MUD PACK FOR OILY SKIN

1 tablespoon fuller's earth	1 small carton natural yoghurt

First thoroughly clean the face.

Mix the earth with the yoghurt, to form a paste.

Apply to the face and neck with a paint brush. Spread thickly, using all the mixture.

Leave on for 15 to 20 minutes, then rinse off with lukewarm water and splash the skin with cold water. Pat dry with a warm towel.

This pack will dry up excess oil in the skin.

For *Mud Dry Shampoo*, see p. 43.

Freckles

Freckles are said to be a sign of beauty, but many people disagree. The thinner the skin, the more liable it is to freckle easily. Bathing the skin daily in fresh buttermilk is an excellent remedy for freckles, and will also bring relief from sunburn. To help to disguise freckles on the face, massage a little almond oil or pure olive oil into the skin before applying foundation or powder. All the lotions in this section can also be used to fade age spots and other skin discolourations.

Pliny once said that 'A liniment made with cress applied with vinegar, taketh off all spots and freckles of the visage.' I think that he was probably referring to watercress. Culpeper's advice for a clear unfreckled complexion is 'To eat a handful of watercress daily, and to drink a glass of boiled water before meals.'

BUTTERMILK LOTION

To fade unwanted freckles.

6 tablespoons fresh buttermilk	1 teaspoon freshly grated horseradish

Pour the ingredients together into a bottle and shake well.
Oil the face with a little almond oil.
Apply with cotton wool.
Leave on the skin for 20 minutes, then wash off with warm water.

DANDELION FRECKLE LOTION

Regular washing with this lotion will gradually fade unwanted freckles.

1 cup freshly picked opened dandelion flowers	1½ cups tap water

Put the water and dandelion flowers into a pan and bring to the boil.
Simmer for 30 minutes, then strain through a sieve. Squeeze the flowers well, to get out all the colour, then bottle.
To use: apply to the face with cotton wool. Use day and night. Do not wash off the lotion: allow it to sink into the skin, and watch those freckles fade. Do not be put off by the colour and the smell. I have used this lotion and found that it worked.

ELDERFLOWER FRECKLE LOTION

This lotion will fade unwanted freckles and age spots, and is also a good skin freshener.

1 cup elderflowers   2 cups soft water, boiling

Put the elderflowers into an earthenware jug and pour over the 2 cups of boiling water. Cover the jug and steep overnight.
Strain through a sieve lined with butter muslin, then pour into a bottle.
Shake well before using. Apply to the skin with a pad of cotton wool. Do not wash off. Use daily.

LEMON FRECKLE LOTION

This lotion will help to remove freckles and fade age spots, and will also bring relief from sunburn.

10 tablespoons fresh lemon   10 tablespoons glycerine
    juice   1 tablespoon peroxide of
10 tablespoons rosewater   hydrogen

Pour all the ingredients into a glass bottle. Shake well.
Apply to the face with a pad of cotton wool.
Allow to dry into the skin.
Wash off with warm milk, then splash the face with cold water to close open pores and pat dry with a warm towel.

MILK AND LEMON LOTION

This lotion will help to disguise the freckles, and it will also soften and refine the skin. With the fresh smell of lemon, it is pleasant to use, even if a bit runny.

1 cup of milk   2 slices fresh lemon

Put the lemon slices into the cup of milk and leave for 3 hours, until the milk has curdled slightly.
Remove the lemon.
Store in the refrigerator, or it will turn sour and begin to smell unpleasant.
Apply the lotion to the skin with cotton wool: do not wash off, but allow to sink into the skin.

Kitchen Remedies for the Skin

EGGS
Eggs can tighten, soften or nourish the skin when added to different remedies.

EGG AND HONEY SKIN CLEANSER

This cleansing mask will deeply cleanse the pores, soften and nourish the skin. Recommended for dry skin.

1 fresh egg yolk   1 teaspoon olive oil
1 tablespoon honey

Mix all the ingredients together in a bowl to form a paste.
Using a soft pastry brush, lightly spread over the face.
Leave on for 15 minutes.
Remove with cotton wool that has been soaked in warm water.
Finish by splashing the skin with cold water, then pat dry with a soft towel.
Moisturise the skin well.

EGG AND SALT DEEP CLEANSER

Recommended for oily skin. This will open pores, cleanse deeply and thoroughly, and remove the dead skin cells which cause blackheads and spots.

1 egg white
1 teaspoon lemon juice

1 tablespoon coarse sea salt

Using a hand whisk, beat the egg white and lemon juice together into a firm froth, then slowly fold in the sea salt.
Apply this mixture to the face very quickly, before the salt has time to dissolve. Gently rub into the face in small circular movements, using the tips of your fingers, to remove any dead skin cells on the skin's surface.
Rinse off straight away with warm water.
Wash the face several times with cold water. Pat dry, then tone and moisturise as normal.

EGG AND WHEATGERM TO NOURISH AND SOFTEN

Recommended for all skin types.

1 small egg	1 teaspoon almond oil
2 tablespoons wheatgerm	

Beat together the egg and almond oil.
Fold in the wheatgerm, to form a stiff paste.
Gently massage all the mixture onto the face.
Leave on for 5–8 minutes.
Rinse thoroughly with warm water.

HONEY

Honey is one of the oldest remedies for skin, going back for centuries: and not only as a beauty treatment. Honey is a natural preserver, and the ancient Egyptians used to embalm their dead bodies in honey to prevent decomposition. Honey is also a wonderful cleanser, whatever your skin type. It is ideal for dry skin, gentle enough to use on sensitive skin and a natural healer for oily, spotty skin.

HONEY CLEANSER

For all skin types.

Heat 4 tablespoons of honey.
Using your fingertips, massage gently into the skin.
Leave on for 15 minutes.
Remove with a soft tissue, then rinse with warm water.

Finish by splashing the skin with cold water to close any enlarged pores, pat the face dry with a warm towel and moisturise well.

HONEY AND CREAM FACE MASK

Recommended for dry skin.

1 tablespoon double cream   4 tablespoons honey, warmed

Add cream to honey and mix together well.
Massage gently onto the face, well into the skin.
Leave 15–20 minutes.
Rinse off with warm water.
Apply a good rich cream moisturiser.

HONEY AND WHEATGERM MASK

A good natural toning cream, recommended for badly blemished skin.

1 tablespoon wheatgerm   4 tablespoons honey, warmed

Add wheatgerm to honey.
Massage well into the skin.
Leave on for 20 minutes.

Firstly remove with a tissue, then wash off with warm water. Pat the face dry with a warm soft towel. *Do not* splash the face with cold water or apply any moisturiser to the skin.

Exercising and Massaging the Face

Just as your body benefits from regular exercise, so will your face. During the day you carry out natural facial exercises all the time. Activities like talking, smiling and eating keep the muscles in the face working.

Gently exercising and massaging the face will keep the skin supple and your features young-looking. Not only will a massage help to keep tiny wrinkles and lines at bay, it will also relieve the tension which causes wrinkles, especially around the eyes. It is also very relaxing.

To stimulate and refresh the skin, it is best to exercise the face first thing in the morning, just after you have woken up. If you want to relax and brush away tension, then massage the face at night, just after a bath, before going to bed.

Some simple movements to massage the face are given below. It is a good idea to sit in front of a mirror and practice the facial movements, then in time you will be able to massage the face with your eyes closed, which is the best way to massage any part of the body: relaxed and with the eyes lightly closed, sitting or lying comfortably.

GIVE YOURSELF A FACE MASSAGE
1) First remove all make-up and thoroughly cleanse the whole face.

2) Brush and tie the hair back away from the face.
3) Use a light cream or moisturiser, or a little olive oil or glycerine, if it agrees with your skin type.
4) Always use the tips of the fingers when massaging.

First exercise   Relax the whole face, lightly close your lips and allow the jaw to fall naturally. Relax the tongue, letting it lie gently in the mouth. Massage both sides of the face together. Using the second and third fingertips, gently stroke the skin starting from the laughter lines around the mouth. Stroke up to the nose, then outwards across the cheekbones to the temples. Repeat this 10 times.

Second exercise   Keep the hands flat and the fingers together. Place your left hand onto the centre of the forehead, and your right hand lightly over your right eye. Gently stroke the forehead upwards with your right hand, following the same movements with your left hand, so you are constantly stroking the forehead using both hands. Continue to do this for 3–5 minutes.

Third exercise   With the eyes closed, using the second and third fingertips only, gently circle around the temple area, massaging both sides at the same time. Repeat this 20 times, 10 times each side.

Fourth exercise   Using the third fingertips only, and with very soft gentle strokes, move outwards, across the browbone, underneath the eyes, and then back over the lids. Repeat 5 times for each eye.

FACIAL EXERCISES
Are you a frowner?

Most people frown all the time, without knowing it. People usually frown when they are watching the television, or if they're sewing or knitting. Most of us frown when we are reading, working or concentrating on something studious.

1)   Smooth those furrows by using the palm of your hand to push back the scalp, away from the hairline. Hold each stroke for the count of 3. Repeat this 10 times.

2)   Hard work and too many late nights will lead to baggy, puffy lids. This quick and simple exercise is excellent for removing puffiness. First thing in the morning, as soon as you have opened your eyes, close them again, very tightly, and screw the eyes up hard. Keeping the eyes closed, raise the eyebrows and stretch the eyelids upwards, as far as they will go without actually opening. Then slowly lower the eyebrows, open the eyes and relax the face. Repeat five times more.

3)   This exercise is for smoothing the laughter lines, which run from the nose to the mouth. Keeping the mouth closed, puff the cheeks out with air. Roll the air around inside the mouth in a circle. Do this for 3–5 minutes.

4)   When tension strikes, it is almost always in the neck muscles. To relieve tension in the neck, drop the head to the left side of the chest with a little bounce. Raise the head, and drop to the right side of the chest. Repeat this 5 times.

5)   This is also a very good exercise to relax the neck and face muscles. Simply roll the head gently and very slowly in a circle. First roll the head in one direction, then the other. Keep the eyes closed and try to stretch the neck as you roll the head. Repeat 6 times each side.

6)   Lines around the mouth are usually caused by tension and stress. People that are nervous, unsettled and worried tend to purse their lips together, and to hold them tightly once closed. To prevent these lines, open the mouth as wide as possible and throw the head back. Relax the mouth and bring the head forward. Now, keeping the head level, open and close the mouth really wide. Repeat this 10 times.

AGING SKIN

Unfortunately it is true that a woman's skin will wrinkle far quicker and earlier than a man's. This is due to their hormones. Men produce more sebum and have greasier skin than women. This provides a man's skin with a protective layer, which helps to stave off wrinkles and lines. Women's skin tends to be a lot finer and dryer, and is therefore more prone to wrinkle. However, at around the age of 45 men will start to catch up. Their skin begins to wrinkle little by little, and as a man's skin is thicker, their lines and wrinkles will be a lot deeper.

Wrinkles are due to the shrinking of fatty tissues beneath the skin. As the tissues shrink and shrivel up, the skin covering them falls into little lines and wrinkles, more or less according to the amount of fatty tissue which has shrunk and the type of skin you have. Some skins are naturally more elastic than others. Generally the lines that form at the side of the mouth, running from the nose to the mouth, are the deepest, as it is on the cheeks that there is generally the greatest loss of fatty tissue. When young, the cheeks are full and round, and the skin over them taut, but as the years pass the tissue deteriorates, and the cheeks either become hollow or flabby, and deep lines form. The fine lines and wrinkles that form around the eyes and beneath them are often due to a too dry skin, and very dry skin is prone to wrinkle early on in life.

The sun's rays can cause premature aging. The best protection is to wear a rich cream moisturiser that contains a sunscreen. Better still, gently massage into the skin a little rosewater and glycerine.

HAIR

Hair is said to be 'One's own crown and glory!'

The first step to healthy-looking hair is a good trim every 6 weeks, followed by regular shampooing, conditioning, massaging and exercising, to keep it soft, shiny, free from dandruff and attractive-looking.

Hot weather makes the hair swell, and it will seem fuller. In the summer the hair is physically thicker, as the hair works in cycles, falling out in the autumn, then growing again in the warmer weather. There is less elasticity in the hair during the hotter months, since the outdoor humidity provides a fine moisture barrier to smooth down the hair's surface moisture cuticle.

If you do need to shampoo your hair frequently, particularly if it is fine and cut short, it is best to use a herbal shampoo, as it will be mild and gentle, and will condition the hair as well as thoroughly cleaning it, leaving it soft, sweet smelling and with a natural shine. Unlike many other shampoos that contain a detergent base, a herbal shampoo will not leave your hair feeling dry.

Dull, dry, damaged hair can be caused by many things, the most obvious being too much heat from using hair driers, hot tongs, heated rollers and styling wands. Too much heat will damage the outer cuticles, causing the ends to become brittle and easily split. When drying your hair, bear in mind that when the hair is wet it is at its weakest, because the hydrogen bonds, one of the two types of bonds that hold the hair together, are broken. The other bonds are the disulphide bonds: these are only broken in permanent waving.

After washing, make sure to condition the ends of the hair well, especially if you are to use rollers, which could buckle the ends of the hair unless a conditioner is used to soften and give each shaft a protective coating. Never tug hard at the hair when wet, and whenever possible allow it to dry naturally.

If you have oily-lank hair that tends to cling to the scalp, either go for a first class cut or try a perm, which will help to stop the greasiness by lifting the hair away from the scalp and will also slightly dry the hair.

A good perm can transform you, but although a perm is easy to keep in shape, it also needs a lot of looking after. A permanent waving lotion will change the natural structure of the hair, and reset it into a new shape; but during this process some of the hair might be damaged or made more brittle. The hair's outer layer (cuticle) may be roughened, so that more moisture escapes, and the hair will absorb light rather than reflect it: in other words, permed hair is in danger of being dry, dull and easily damaged.

If this is the case, it is important to use a mild shampoo, one which will spread over the hair easily and evenly without further roughening the hair's surface. After shampooing the hair, rinse under a powerful spray if possible, as water pressure is the best way of ridding the hair of debris. A perm will need a trim every 6 weeks. If the hair starts to frizz, apply setting lotion to help it to relax after washing and tame it gently with a hot brush. To freshen the hair, use a gel when damp and dry with a low heat, scrunching the hair with your hands while drying.

Hair may also be badly damaged by the sun. When the hair is waterlogged from the sea it will become very sensitive, and the sun's ultraviolet rays have a 20% higher damaging effect on wet hair. When out of the water the combination of sea and sun will dry the skin as well as the hair. If the hair has been permed, bleached or coloured, it is prone to soak up the sun and the water more quickly than normal, straight, unchemically treated hair. The sun can both help and harm the hair. A little will help to bring out the natural highlights in any type of hair, but at the same time the combination of sun, sea, wind and chlorine will dry it out, eventually causing it to become dry and dull-looking, with badly split ends. When out in the sun for a long time, apply a little olive oil to the ends of the hair. This will help to stop the ends from splitting, and will protect it from dryness.

Men are notoriously lazy when it comes to hair care, and will use any old shampoo that ccomes to hand, regardless of its suitability. So keep an eye on him and make sure that he is using a shampo that is right for his hair type: he will thank you for it in the end. How often a man should shampoo his hair depends on a number of things: whether he lives in the city, if the hair is dry or oily, or if he is an active person who perspires a lot. The average man will probably only need to wash his hair twice a week. Men who have oily hair and need to wash it daily to keep it looking clear and at its best should use only the mildest of shampoos, as washing the hair every day with a strong shampoo will lead to brittle, dull, lifeless hair, as the oil which is secreted by the scalp and which is a natural conditioner is lost.

Have you ever wondered what your hair would look like

if it was a different colour? Have you ever tried a hair colourant, but were disappointed with the results? A change of colour can be a difficult decision to make, but it needn't be. Lots of women were blonde when they were younger, but in time the hair has become what can only be described as a 'dishwater blonde'. The last thing that you want is to end up looking 'bleached' or 'brassy' and having to re-touch the roots every 3 to 4 weeks. The delight of herbal dyes is that you can lighten or darken your hair very gradually, and no-one will know. As herbs are so mild and gentle, they will only bring out the natural highlights in your hair.

Using a herbal solution, which is chemical-free, is nature's way to add extra shine and to enhance your own hair colour naturally.

Shampoos

EGG SHAMPOO

An egg shampoo is very beneficial for hair that is turning grey or for brown hair, as the sulphur in the yolk helps to arrest greyness and will bring out the natural red in brown hair.

2 or 3 eggs	1 tablespoon fine
1 tablespoon white wine	shredded soap
vinegar	(unscented)
	1 teaspoon bay rum

Beat up 2 or 3 or more eggs, depending on the length of the hair.

Add 1 tablespoon of lukewarm water for each egg.

Add the soap and bay rum while beating. Beat until it becomes a foamy mass.

Shampoo the hair as normal. Rinse off three times, adding a tablespoon of white wine vinegar to the final rinse.

OLIVE OIL SHAMPOO

For all hair types.

½ pint boiling water	2 tablespoons olive oil
4 tablespoons dried rosemary leaves	2 tablespoons castor oil

Put the rosemary leaves into a jug and pour over the boiling water.

Cover and leave to infuse for 1 hour.

Pour the olive and castor oils into a bottle, shaking thoroughly.

Strain the infusion and add to the bottled oils. Screw the top on tightly and shake for 3 minutes.

Massage into wet hair. Leave on for 10 minutes, then rinse off.

SOAPWORT SHAMPOO

This shampoo is recommended for grey, blonde and dry hair.

1 pint boiling water	2 tablespoons dried
2 tablespoons dried	soapwort
chamomile flowers	

Put the dried herbs into a glass jug. Pour over the boiling water, cover with a plate or saucer and leave to infuse for 30 minutes.
Strain and bottle.
Wet hair and shampoo in. Leave on for 3–5 minutes, then rinse off.
When in contact with water, the soapwort will produce a natural lather.

EGG AND VINEGAR SHAMPOO

This is a good shampoo for dry, grey hair, or if you suffer from dandruff.

2 large fresh egg yolks	2 tablespoons cider
	vinegar

Add the vinegar to the egg yolks and beat together.
Wet the hair and simply massage in the eggs. Leave on for 10 minutes then rinse off. If you have long hair, double the ingredients.

A MUD DRY SHAMPOO

As fuller's earth has excellent absorbent properties, it makes an ideal dry shampoo.

1 teaspoon of fuller's earth,   eau-de-Cologne
   (in powder form)

Sprinkle the powder onto the greasy roots, then brush the powder through the hair, using a firm bristle brush, working down away from the scalp. Finish by spraying the hair with your favourite eau-de-Cologne, to give added freshness and shine.

Conditioners

CONDITIONER FOR BLONDE HAIR

Chamomile will highlight the hair, and the effect is better and more natural than any chemical hair dye. Although chamomile shampoos and rinses are usually only for blonde hair, I have found that this conditioner works just as well for brunettes. I have used it, and my hair is a dark reddish-brown colour. It left my hair soft and clean, with a glossy shine.

2 tablespoons dried   juice of 1 fresh lemon
   chamomile flowers   2 egg yolks
½ pint water, boiling

Put the dried chamomile flowers into a glass or china container, pour over the ½ pint of boiling water and leave to infuse for 3 hours.
Strain the infusion.
Add the lemon juice and bottle, shaking well.
Beat the egg yolks in a bowl.
Add 2 tablespoons of the liquid to the egg yolks and mix in thoroughly.
Wash the hair as normal. Massage the egg and lemon into the hair and leave on for 15 minutes. Rinse off using the infusion of chamomile, water and lemon juice. Allow the hair to dry naturally in the sun.

PARSLEY AND SAGE CONDITIONER

This rinse is guaranteed to add shine to all types of hair.

2 tablespoons bruised
   parsley leaves
2 tablespoons bruised sage
   leaves

1 pint soft water, boiling

Put the leaves into an earthenware jug and pour over the boiling water.
Cover the jug with a saucer and leave for 30 minutes.
Strain and bottle when cool.

Rinses and Tonics

ROSEMARY AND SAGE RINSE

This rinse is recommended for oily hair.

2 tablespoons dried
  rosemary leaves
1 tablespoon dried sage
  leaves

1 ¾ pints boiling water
2 tea bags

Mix the sage and rosemary leaves and the tea bags together in an earthenware jug.
Pour over the boiling water and cover with a saucer.
Leave to stand for 30 minutes.
Strain through a sieve into another jug, cover and allow to cool before bottling.
Use as a final rinse to add extra shine and body and to leave your hair with the sweet smell of rosemary.

NETTLE HAIR FRESHENER

This lotion will give your hair a natural shine and help to mend split ends.

1 cup of freshly picked nettle
  leaves
1 pint boiling water

¼ cup cider vinegar
¼ cup eau-de-Cologne

Steep leaves overnight in boiling water.
Add the vinegar and cologne.
Shake well and bottle.
Use this rinse three times a week, massaging well into the scalp.

HAIR TONIC FOR DANDRUFF

This remedy is very simple to make, and effective: when used regularly it will clear up dandruff. Use three times a week.

4 tablespoons dried rosemary leaves	2 pints soft water, boiling

Put the rosemary leaves into an earthenware jug or china container. Pour over the boiling water, cover and leave to infuse for 3 hours.
Strain into a bottle and shake.
Use as a final rinse after the hair has been washed. Pour the rinse over the hair several times. Enough for two final rinses: double the quantities if the hair is long.

ONION TO MAKE THE HAIR GROW

3 large onions 3 large cloves of garlic	4 tablespoons clear honey

Add the juice of the onion and garlic to the honey and mix together well.

Shampoo the hair as normal and towel dry. While the hair is damp, rub the mixture into it, massaging well into the roots. Leave for 10 minutes. Rinse off with warm water.

Provided that the mixture is applied regularly, not only will it make the hair grow more quickly, it will also help change grey hair to black.

Natural Hair Colours

CHAMOMILE RINSE FOR BLONDE HAIR

1 handful dried chamomile 1 ¾ pints boiling water
   flowers

Pour the boiling water over the flowers and leave for 30 minutes.

Strain into an earthenware jug and cover.

Bottle when cool. Pour rinse several times over the hair, to soften and add to your natural colour.

ELDER TO DARKEN THE HAIR

This is a very old Roman remedy.

3 handfuls ripe elderberries 1 pint white wine

Add the berries to the wine and bring to the boil; simmer
for 30 minutes.
Remove from heat and strain through a sieve.
Bottle when cold.
Use as a final rinse after washing the hair.

Mousses and Sprays

ROSE HAIR MOUSSE

This is a good mousse to prevent split ends and to protect
the hair from heat when blow drying.

4 fresh egg whites	2 tablespoons oil of rose
½ pint cold soft water	

Whisk together the egg whites and the water.
Add the oil of rose and beat until it becomes a foamy mass.
To use: apply to the hair after it has been washed and
towel-dried. Comb through the hair, then style or blow dry
as normal.
Rosewater can be used instead of ordinary water. In that
case no oil of rose is required.

QUILLIA TO ADD BODY AND SHINE

This is an old country remedy, dating back to the early 19th
century.

1 oz tincture of quillia   10 drops oil of rosemary
1 oz rectified spirits   5 drops oil of verbena
6 oz rosewater

Mix together the quillia, the spirits and the rosewater.
Add the oils.
Bottle and shake well.
Sprinkle a few drops onto a clean brush and apply to the
hair when dry. It will leave a beautiful gloss, without
making the hair greasy.

HAIR SPRAY

Most of today's hairstyles need to be kept firmly in place
with a strong hairspray, but hairspray used daily will dry
the hair, make it more greasy and cause a dry scalp and
dandruff. This hairspray will hold your hair, and it is mild
and gentle enough to use daily, without worrying about
damaging your hair.

2 large fresh lemons   2 tablespoons vodka
2 cups water

Slice the lemons and boil fast in the water, until the liquid is
halved.
Strain and bottle, adding the vodka to preserve the lotion.
Pour into a plant sprayer, shaking well before use.
Use to hold your style in place. This works best on
natural-looking, scrunch-dried hair.

A Favourite Herb: Rosemary

Rosemary is one of my favourite herbs. It is widely cultivated in gardens and valued for its pleasant scent. Gypsies peddle sprigs of rosemary, which is also known as Queen of Hungary, world wide. It is a charm against evil. Gypsies hang rosemary sprigs around the windows and doors of their caravans as a protection against witches, and put a sprig under their children's beds, to prevent them from having nightmares.

ROSEMARY SHAMPOO

1 bottle (125 ml) mild and unscented shampoo
4 tablespoons rosemary leaves

¼ pint rain water, boiling

Put the leaves into an earthenware jug and pour over the boiling rain water.
Cover and leave to stand for 20 minutes.
Strain and mix the rosemary infusion with the shampoo, beating together well. A liquidiser is a great help.
Bottle and use as a normal shampoo.

ROSEMARY HAIR RINSE

The rosemary shampoo and this rinse are ideal for brunettes, bringing out the natural colour in their hair.

| 1 cup rosemary sprigs | 2 tea bags |
| 1 ¾ pints soft water | |

Boil the water. While simmering, add the sprigs and tea bags.

Pour into an earthenware jug, cover and leave for 20 minutes.

Strain and bottle while still warm.

To use: rinse hair, cover the head with a warm towel and leave for a few minutes, then rinse off.

This rinse, used after the rosemary shampoo, will leave your hair shiny and soft, with a sweet smell of rosemary.

ROSEMARY HAIR TONIC

This tonic is ideal for dry hair, and will remove dandruff.

| 4 tablespoons spirits of rosemary | 5 tablespoons surgical spirits |
| 4 teaspoons castor oil | 3 tablespoons lavender water |

Mix together and bottle, shaking well.

Apply to the scalp after washing the hair, massaging thoroughly. Comb through the hair and rinse off with warm water.

ROSEMARY TO MAKE THE HAIR GROW THICKER

1 cup rosemary flowers and
  tops
2 pints white wine

16 tablespoons honey
¼ pint sweet almond oil

Steep the rosemary in the wine for 8 hours.
Add the honey and sweet almond oil and stir the mixture
thoroughly, until the honey has dissolved into the liquid.
Pour into a jar while still warm.
To use: put 2–3 tablespoons into a cup and stand the cup in
a pan of water. Heat until blood warm.
Massage into the scalp and comb through the hair. Leave
for 20 minutes, then rinse off.

ROSEMARY HEAD RUB

Rosemary is exceptional for hair care. It is a natural
conditioner, and prevents dandruff and hair loss.

4 tablespoons almond oil

4 tablespoons oil of
  rosemary

Heat the almond oil in a cup standing in a pan of boiling
water.
Add the oil of rosemary and stir.
Massage the warm oil into the scalp before washing the hair
with a rosemary shampoo.

ROSEMARY SCALP MASSAGE

2 tablespoons oil of rosemary	4 tablespoons coconut oil
4 tablespoons castor oil	1 teaspoon oil of jasmine

Heat the oils, except the oil of jasmine, together in a cup standing in a pan of warm water. Warm on a low heat for a few minutes.

Stir thoroughly, remove from heat and pour into a bottle. Add the oil of jasmine and shake well.

Use before washing. Massage the warm oil into the scalp and comb through the hair. Leave for 5 minutes, then rinse off.

Massaging the scalp increases circulation and is very beneficial for the hair and scalp. Massaging it with oil is a pleasure and worth the few extra minutes before shampooing.

These are just examples of how you can make your own shampoos, rinses and conditioners. Once you know how to make your own, you can experiment until you find a herb and fragrance that you particularly like. My favourites are the rosemary shampoo and rinse, because they leave my hair soft, with the sweet smell of rosemary, and bring out the natural red in my hair.

Lavender shampoo is another of my favourites. It can easily be made by using the same ingredients and method as the rosemary shampoo: simply use 4 tablespoons of lavender flowers instead of the rosemary leaves.

To make a lavender hair tonic, use instead 4 tablespoons

of oil of lavender and 3 tablespoons of rose oil or rose water.

Or you could use lemon balm, mint, lemon verbena leaves or thyme. The same applies for the rinse.

When using oils to massage into the scalp, it is best to warm slightly before using, but do not heat the oil too much, as the scalp is very sensitive.

I have tried all the remedies listed here myself, except for a few which I gave to family and friends to try. They were all pleased with the results. They are fun to make, and safe to use.

Washing a Child's Hair

Most children are quite happy to spend hours playing in the bath, but only too ready to throw a temper tantrum when it comes to washing the hair. This becomes a nightmare for everyone, who will eventually dread bathtime.

Here are a few tips on how to wash children's hair, without tears and tantrums.

EASY WAYS TO WASH A CHILD'S HAIR

1) The best way to shampoo a child's hair is in the bath with a shower attachment.

2) Give the child a dry face flannel to hold over the eyes, to protect from any drips.

3) Make a shield over the eyes, using your thumb and forefinger, and keep the head gently tilted back.

4) Don't allow the hair to get wringing wet, as the shampoo will run.

5)   Use a mild, unperfumed shampoo, so if any should get into the eyes, it won't sting so much.

6)   To give the child more control, let him or her massage in the shampoo by himself.

7)   When rinsing the hair, with the head still backwards, scrape the scalp towards the back of the head, to stop any trickles over the face.

8)   If your child doesn't like the face flannel over the eyes, catch his or her attention and make him look up by hanging a spring bug over the bath, so he can watch it while it bobs around; or a colourful mobile; or stick a large transfer to the ceiling; or, if you are artistic, paint a favourite cartoon character onto the ceiling.

Exercising the Hair and Massaging the Scalp

You wash and condition your hair regularly, but do you exercise it? Regular brushing is vital, whatever the length of the hair. Brushing the hair will stimulate the scalp and encourage healthy hair growth. It keeps the sebaceous glands working and gives shine to dry hair. Brushing will relax the nerves and muscles and help to prevent tension, which causes the hair to fall out.

These exercises are not only beneficial for the hair and scalp: they are also very relaxing.

1)   Always use a soft bristle brush, and brush the hair 50 times every night.

2)   First brush the hair straight down starting from the roots.

3)   Now tilt the head to the left, and brush the right side of the hair over the head to the left, then tilt the head to the right, and brush the left side of the hair over to the right. Do this 10 times each side.

4)   Sit in a chair and lean your head forward, so that you are looking down at the floor. Starting from the back of the neck, brush the hair over the head, brushing the hair forward. Do this 10 times.

5)   Finish by brushing the hair straight down starting from the forehead, brushing the hair backwards. Tilt the head and look up while doing this. Brush 10 times.

MASSAGING THE SCALP

The benefits of massaging the scalp are very similar to the benefits of brushing the hair. It is good for the scalp and very relaxing.

1)   Always massage the scalp when the hair is dry, before washing. First dip the fingertips into a bowl of warm olive oil or a mild hair conditioner.

2)   Push the fingertips through the hair, directly onto the scalp.

3)   Massage into the skin firmly using small circular movements, paying special attention to the temples and the nape of the neck.

4)   Massage the scalp for 4–5 minutes, then wash and condition the hair as normal.

RELAXATION

Hair loss is often caused by nervous tension and stress. To avoid this, take time in the day to sit down somewhere quiet and relax; or, when you feel tense, go for a walk or have a chat with a friend over a cup of tea or coffee; or, even better, take up yoga, which is very relaxing.

Most women lose hair just after having a baby. This is because when you are pregnant the hormones interrupt the natural growing cycle of the hair. The hair that you would normally have shed from day to day stays on. Through the 9 months the hair will look its best, but it will fall out after having the baby. After a while, the cycle will settle down, and hair growth will return to normal.

Like the weather, certain drugs can affect your hair, either making it dry or greasy, or making it lose its natural shine.

Grey hair tends to be dry, as it has lost most of the natural oils which keep hair shiny and healthy-looking, and in good condition. For grey hair, give the scalp an oil rub and a massage 3 times a week; or, better still, wash the hair with 3 eggs, and use ½ pint of warm water with 1 cup of freshly squeezed lemon juice added to rinse.

Extra Tips for Hair Care

1) Have a good cut every 6 months, and have the ends cut every 6 weeks.
2) Washing the hair every day will eventually wash out the hair's natural oils. Twice a week is enough to keep the hair looking its best. If you do have to wash your hair more frequently, it is best to use a mild herbal shampoo, which will not leave your hair dry, as, unlike other shampoos, it does not contain a detergent base.
3) Never tug at your hair when it is wet and at its weakest. Instead gently comb through in sections, using a wide-toothed comb.

4) Try using beer instead of setting lotion. Rinse the hair through with 1 cup of beer after washing, then dry and style hair as normal.

5) Massaging the scalp will make the hair healthier. Use the tips of your fingers or a brush to loosen dead skin cells.

6) At least twice a week, after washing the hair, allow it to dry naturally. Sit in a warm room, or better still sit out in the sun. Never sit and dry the hair in front of a fire! It will only scorch the hair, causing split ends.

7) Hair driers, hot styling brushes and hair sprays will dry the hair, cause split ends and eventually cause it to lose its natural shine. After washing, condition the hair well and finish by adding ½ pint of fresh lemon juice to 1 pint of warm water. Use this as a final rinse. Pour over the hair several times, to protect the hair from heat.

8) Before washing the hair, give it a good brush and massage the scalp with warm oil, using the tips of the fingers.

9) To keep the hair tangle-free, brush 50 times every night, using a soft bristle brush. It is very relaxing, especially if someone else is doing it for you. It will help to calm the nerves, and aid sleep.

EYES

Beautiful eyes can make even a plain face attractive. If you do not possess large expressive eyes, you can still make them clear and bright with the proper care and attention.

Never work in a strong light, or read in a poor light. Both are equally bad for the eyesight. When reading or working, allow the light to fall onto the book or paper. Make sure that all light bulbs are well-shaded. A light that is too strong and bright is very trying to the eyes.

An old superstition says, 'If you wear a fresh-opened dandelion every day behind the right ear, you will never have cause to wear glasses.'

Eye Baths & Fresheners

EYE BATH

Give the eyes a bath daily, and always after being exposed to fog, dust or a long car journey. The eye wash should be warm, and fresh lotion used for each eye.

1 5ml spoon boric acid powder	1 tablespoon rosewater
½ pint water, boiled	

Dissolve the acid powder in the water.
Add the rosewater.

Pour into a clean bottle, shaking well.
Use daily.

For tired eyes
If the eyes feel dull and tired, take two cotton wool pads
squeezed out in boric acid lotion, and place over the closed
eyes; or use two cold tea bags, or two cotton wool pads that
have been squeezed out in fennel juice.

FRESHENER FOR TIRED EYES

This is very refreshing and relaxing for tired eyes.

1 cotton hanky	eau-de-Cologne
warm water	

Soak the hanky in the warm water, then wring out. Fold it
like a bandage, and sprinkle a few drops of eau-de-Cologne
onto it.
Lay the hanky lightly over the closed eyes and sit with your
head back in a dark room for 10 minutes. This will refresh
and brighten the eyes.

Tips for Eye Beauty

EYEBROWS
Brush the eyebrows every night to prevent dandruff
amongst the roots, which will eventually spoil them.

Use two soft brushes, one to apply, the other to dry.

Dip the brush into a little almond oil and brush the brow upwards away from the eye. Then, using the dry brush, brush across. Sweep straight across the brow, following its natural line.

TO DARKEN THE EYEBROWS

Most women who have light eyebrows use a black or brown eye pencil to make the eyebrows look darker, but you can darken your eyebrows naturally. Regular application of yellow vaseline rubbed into them three times a day will darken them. You will see the difference in five weeks.

PLUCKING EYEBROWS

Unless they are extremely thick, it is best not to start plucking the eyebrows. Regular plucking over the years will weaken them. Some won't grow back at all, and those that do will be fine and weak. So do so if you must, but be careful not to over-pluck.

Here are a few tips.

1) Never pluck above the brow: it will spoil the natural outline.

2) Always pluck the same way that the hair grows.

3) To tidy up the eyebrows, just remove the few stragglers that grow across the bridge of your nose, and from beneath the brow.

4) After you have plucked the eyebrows, massage them with a little olive or almond oil.

EYELASHES

Long, dark eyelashes add beauty to the eyes.

To make the eyelashes grow longer and thicker, remove

all trace of eye make-up. With your eyes closed, apply a little yellow vaseline to the lashes. Open them, and, with the tips of your fingers, gently bend the lashes upwards to cover the roots. Leave on overnight. Wash off in the morning with a little warm water, followed by an eye bath.

EYELIDS
To keep the eyelids light, smooth and unwrinkled, bathe the lids with cold water in the morning and massage with sweet almond oil at night.

To massage the eyelids, close one eye, and, with the second fingertip moistened with a little almond oil, gently stroke upwards to the outer corner, then lightly sweep across the lid with a cotton wool pad to remove the oil. Then treat the other eyelid.

If the oil enters the eye, bathe with warm, then cold water. It will do the eye no harm, but it will be uncomfortable.

HOLLOWS BENEATH THE EYES
The skin around the eyes should never be rubbed, as it is the finest and most delicate skin on the face and is easily stretched. To fill out hollows beneath the eyes, spread a good face cream thickly and allow to soak into the skin. Do not wash it off. Leave on until morning, then remove gently with warm water.

THE WHITES OF THE EYES
The whites of the eyes should be clear. Any sign of redness means strain on the eyes, and maybe a slight cold in the eyes. A yellow tinge in the eyes is a sign of the 'liver.'

To remove a yellow tinge in the eyes, drink a glass of

water with the juice of 1 fresh lemon added each morning instead of a cup of tea or coffee.

For bright eyes, eat a fresh sprig of parsley three times a day.

Exercises for the Eyes

To keep the eyes bright and in good condition, they should be exercised daily as well as bathed.

1) First stand up straight, with the head up and the eyes level.

2) Look to your right as far as possible without turning your head.

3) Now look to your left, to the right, then to the left again.

4) Repeat 10 times.

Repeat this simple exercise several times:

Stand straight and, without moving your head, look upwards, then look downwards, as quickly as possible.

LIPS

Do you exercise your lips?

It's not just the body that benefits from exercise: lips need to be exercised as well to keep them in good condition. This sequence of 5 exercises will keep the lips in good shape, improve their colour and keep them soft and supple. The exercises will also tone up your face muscles, firm up flab, tighten sags and keep your face in good condition.

10–Minute Work–out

Stand up straight, or sit erect in front of a mirror.

1) With your lips gently closed, lift the side of your mouth so that you are smiling on the right side of your face. Relax. Do the same on the left side. Repeat 10 times each side.

2) With the mouth slightly open, curl your upper lip over your upper teeth and your lower lip over your bottom teeth. Now try to smile. You should feel the muscles around the mouth pulling. Hold for 3 seconds, then relax the mouth. Repeat 6 times.

3) Keeping your eyes open, open your mouth as wide as you can. Hold for 10 seconds, then relax. Repeat this 5 times.

4) Shut your eyes lightly: try not to screw them up tight. Gently put your head back and, with your mouth closed, smile as widely as you can. Hold this for 5 seconds, then relax. Repeat 5 times.

5) Purse your lips together as if you are about to whistle, but keep the lips tightly closed. With your shoulders straight, look up to the ceiling. Hold this for 3 seconds, then relax the mouth, before repeating 5 times.

As the mouth and lips have been stretched, your lips will be dry and rough. Relax the mouth by gently letting the mouth open naturally and the jaw drop down. Massage with a good cream, wipe off with a cotton wool pad, then apply vaseline thickly.

YELLOWISH TEETH

Natural yellowish teeth are said to be far stronger than pearl white ones; however, if you are a smoker and still want a bright 'Osmond' smile, a clever choice of lipstick will help to make your teeth look whiter.

Use medium to dark colours for contrast.

Colours to choose	*Colours to avoid*
bright reds	oranges
deep reds	corals
fuchsia pinks	frosted pinks
medium plums	golds

Lip Tricks & Tips for Lips

1) Keep your lips free from dead skin with regular exfoliation. Apply a little lip balm during the day when they feel dry, and massage with almond oil at night.

2) Never bite your lips, and avoid licking them to keep

them moist. The water will just evaporate, causing rapid cracking and even sores.

3)   Smoking will eventually give you unattractive wrinkles around the mouth. Stop smoking and take up smiling; or each night relax the mouth and lips and gently massage a little glycerine mixed with a little rosewater into the corners of your mouth.

4)   Massage your lips when moisturising your face, to keep them soft and supple.

5)   Enlarge small lips by outlining them with a dark lip pencil.

6)   Black skin looks great in 'Vamp' red lipstick, and fabulous in bright or deep purply pinks.

7)   To really bring your lips to life, blend a little gold shadow into the centre of your lips before blotting them.

8)   A little extra effort when applying lipstick will make a big difference to staying-on power. Before applying lipstick, first soften the lips with a little clear vaseline or face cream (unscented), then sponge with warm water. Finish by dusting the lips over with a little translucent powder, using a large soft brush.

9)   After applying lipstick, blot, then paint over with a little lipstick shield, and you'll eat, drink and kiss the night away, without the colour budging at all.

HANDS, NAILS & FEET

Creams & Lotions for the Hands

USING HAND CREAMS
When using hand cream in the winter, heat the cream gently in a jar standing in a pan of hot water. Massage gently into the joints with a circular movement and rub the back of the hands well to tone up the muscles. When the hands become red this is a good sign: it shows that the circulation of the blood is being increased, which will generally improve the skin.

UNSCENTED HAND CREAM

This simple cream is excellent for dry, wrinkled hands.

   1 oz zinc ointment   ½ oz olive oil
   1 oz pure lanolin

Melt the zinc and lanolin together in a jar standing in a pan of boiling water.
Add the olive oil and beat to a cream.

Store in a pot or glass jar.

This remedy is centuries old, handed down to me by my grandmother, who can remember helping her great-grandmother make it when she was a child.

ROSE HAND CREAM

To refine and soften the hands, leaving a slight scent of roses.

1 lb lard	2 teaspoons oil of roses
4 tablespoons rosewater	

Put the lard into a basin and pour over enough boiling water to cover. Leave until the water becomes cold, then repeat the process until the lard has been melted three or four times.

Put the melted lard into another clean basin, add the rosewater and beat well, adding the oil of rose while beating to a cream.

Store in a pot or screw-topped jar.

Use daily.

When making the rose hand cream and the rose cleansing cream, it is best to make it near the sink, so that when you have removed the cold water, you can pour the boiling water over before the lard has time to set again.

HONEY HAND CREAM

This is a useful cream to use during the winter to soften rough, chapped hands.

16 tablespoons of honey   16 tablespoons of rose or
                                 lavender water

Heat the honey in an earthenware jug standing in a pan of boiling water.
Slowly stir the rose or lavender water into the honey.
Remove from the heat and store in a screw-topped jar.

HONEY AND VERBENA HAND CREAM

In this cream honey is used to purify and soften the hands, and verbena to scent.

8 tablespoons clear honey   1 teaspoon citric acid
6 drops oil of verbena   1 teaspoon surgical
2 tablespoons glycerine   spirits

Put the honey and glycerine together into a jar standing in warm water and heat gently.
Allow to cool, then stir in the verbena oil a drop at a time.
Add the citric acid and the surgical spirits and blend together well.
Store in a jar or bottle and shake well before use.

LEMON SCENTED HAND CREAM

½ oz beeswax	4 tablespoons sweet
1 handful lemon verbena	almond oil
leaves (dried or fresh)	A pinch of borax
A few drops fresh lemon	4 tablespoons soft water

Steep the verbena leaves overnight in just enough boiling water to cover the leaves. Cover the container with a plate. When cool, strain and bottle.

Add the 4 tablespoons of water and the lemon juice to the infusion and shake well.

Warm the liquid in a pan and dissolve the borax in it.

In a separate pan, melt the beeswax and the sweet almond oil.

Mix all the ingredients together, beating well with a hand whisk or an electric mixer, until the mixture is cool and has a creamy texture, then store.

This sweet-scented cream will leave your hands soft and smooth.

CUCUMBER HAND CREAM

This light green, fresh-smelling cream will leave your hands soft and sweetly scented.

1 cucumber	1 teaspoon glycerine
1 tablespoon witchhazel	1 teaspoon rosewater

Wash and peel the cucumber, and cut into pieces about 1 inch thick.

Mash to a pulp.

Add the witch hazel, rosewater and glycerine, and beat to a cream. A food blender is a great help: mix for 30 seconds, then beat.

Store in a plastic bottle.

Keep it handy by the sink, so that you can use it after doing the washing up, when your hands are dry and need moisturising.

ALMOND HAND LOTION

Almond oil has become the main cosmetic oil, and is successfully used in skin and hair preparations of many types. It is expressed from the kernel of the sweet almond. Traditionally, ripe almonds are ground into a meal, which is used in facial scrubs for its cleansing action. Almond trees that bear white blossom produce bitter almonds, but the tree that bears pink will produce sweet almonds.

Yolk of one large fresh egg
1 tablespoon oil of sweet almonds

1 tablespoon rosewater
50 drops simple tincture of benzoin

Beat up the egg yolk, adding while beating the almond oil and rosewater.

Add the simple tincture of benzoin a drop at a time.

Pour the liquid into a bottle and shake well.

Shake before using. Apply to the hands with a pad of cotton wool. This lotion will soften, scent and freshen the hands.

Kitchen Remedies & Beauty Tips for Hands

Grimy hands can be a big problem for hardworking women, especially keen gardeners. Washing or soaking the hands in hot soapy water isn't usually enough to remove ingrained dirt, and soaking the hands will cause them to become dry and chapped, and make them wrinkle easily.

You won't have to look further than the kitchen shelf for the ingredients for most of these remedies, and those that you may have to buy, like the rosewater and glycerine, will only cost you pennies.

BRAN

Bran is an excellent substitute for soap. It will clean, soften and nourish the hands; oatmeal will also clean the hands.

Wash the hands with warm water. Put 1 tablespoon of bran into the palm of your hand and wash as you would with soap, massaging well into the knuckles and fingers. Dry the hands, then rub in a few drops of olive oil. Finish by dusting with a little fine oatmeal.

LEMON CLEANSER

To really shift ingrained, stubborn stains, wash the hands, dry them well, then rub all over with a thick slice of fresh lemon. It will remove the stains, soften and purify your hands, and leave them with the fresh smell of lemon.

POTATO HAND CREAM

2 medium potatoes
1 tablespoon sweet almond
 oil

1 tablespoon glycerine
1 tablespoon rosewater

Peel, cook and mash the potatoes. Add the remaining ingredients and mix to a paste.

Massage warm into the hands for 15–20 minutes, then wash off.

Store in a container.

Before using again, heat gently and beat to remove lumps in the potato.

Keeps for 1 week.

SUGAR AND SALT

This is enough for one wash, but you could make up a bottleful and leave over the sink, to use when required.

1 tablespoon white sugar
1 tablespoon table or sea salt

2 teaspoons vegetable oil

Mix all the ingredients together.

Massage well into the hands for 5 minutes, then rinse off.

Salt represents life in old folklore, and you should never throw any away. If you do so you are throwing away life itself, which is all too short as it is.

OLD WRINKLED HANDS
When the hands look dry, old and wrinkled, they should be massaged regularly with olive oil or sweet almond oil. This condition is often due to extreme dryness of the skin, rather than old age. Plunging the hands into very hot or very cold water is another cause of dry, wrinkled hands.

Add a little borax to the water when washing clothes: it will help to soften the water. Use a dish mop when washing the dishes, and always wear rubber gloves to protect the hands when in water for a long time. Massage at night with olive oil (slightly warm) mixed with a little witch hazel. Apply a lot and allow to soak into the hands.

TO REFINE THE HANDS

2 egg yolks
1 tablespoon rosewater

1 tablespoon sweet
   almond oil
1 tablespoon lemon juice
   (fresh or bottled)

Beat the egg yolks together and pour into a glass bottle.
Add the rest of the ingredients in the order listed above to the eggs in the bottle, shaking well after each addition.
Wash the hands, then apply the mixture to the hands with a paint brush.
Leave on for 5–8 minutes, then rinse off.

FOR THIN HANDS WITH PROMINENT VEINS
When the hands are too thin and the veins too prominent, it

gives the hands an old, worn look. The best remedy for this is cocoa butter.

Each night wash your hands, and while they are still warm from the water rub in the cocoa butter. Once it touches the palms of the hands it will melt easily. Massage into the hands well. Massage the backs of the hands gently across, then down around the wrists, then finish on the palms.

TO SOFTEN THE HANDS

Glycerine does not agree with every skin type, but when it does it is excellent for refreshing and softening the hands.

Before you use, do a test to see if it will agree with your type of skin. Put a little onto the back of your hand. If it makes the skin go red and smart, then don't use.

Massage a lot into the hands three times a day, working well into the knuckles and base of the fingernails.

REMEDY FOR MOIST HANDS

There is nothing worse than the feeling of hot, sweaty hands, especially during the hot summer months. Here is an old country remedy that might be worth a try.

½ teaspoon alum   ½ pint boiling water

Dissolve the alum in the boiling water and bottle.
Use when needed.
To use: first wash the hands, then apply the lotion with cotton wool. Allow to soak into the hands, then dust the hands with the following:

| 4 tablespoons orris-root powder | 1 teaspoon oil of bergamot |
| 8 tablespoons fine oatmeal | |

Mix all the ingredients thoroughly.
Store in a screw-topped glass jar.
Dust over the hands with a soft brush after they have been washed.

Exercises for the Hands

We can't all avoid arthritic hands and stiff fingerjoints, but you can help to keep the fingers mobile and the wrists strong. If you are young and healthy, do these simple, gentle exercises, to help to prevent stiffness of the joints in later life. If you are overweight or have any back problems, or if you have arthritis, consult your doctor before attempting any of these exercises.

10 MINUTE WORK-OUT FOR THE HANDS

1)   Rest an apple or a soft ball in the palm of your right hand. Tightly clasp your thumb and fingers around the apple (ball), squeezing it as hard you can. Hold for the count of 5, then relax the hand. Then do the same with your left hand. Repeat this exercise 6 times with each hand.

2)   Hold a wooden rolling pin in both hands, with your knuckles facing upwards and your arms stretched out in front of you. Twist your left hand back towards your body, at the same time twisting your right hand away from you. Now twist your left hand away from you and your right

hand back towards you, so that you are turning the rolling pin around. Repeat this 20 times.

3) Hold the rolling pin with both hands with your arms stretched out in front of you. Bend the wrists so your knuckles are facing the floor. Bending only the wrists, curl the rolling pin towards yourself. Now, with your knuckles still facing downwards, turn your hands around so that your knuckles are facing upwards. Curl the rolling pin under, bending only your wrists. Repeat the exercise 10 times in each direction.

4) Finger exercise: press your right thumb and little finger together. Hold for the count of three. Repeat with the thumb, ring finger, middle finger, then first finger. Hold each for the count of three. Repeat this 5 times, then do the same with the left hand, repeating 5 times. Finish by shaking the hands gently to relax.

Tips for Hands

1) To keep the hands soft and supple, massage every night with a tablespoon of honey.

2) To cleanse the hands, rub with a thick slice of raw peeled potato. Leave on for 5 minutes, then rinse off.

3) Freshly squeezed lemon juice will remove stains, soften and purify the hands.

4) Tomato juice makes an excellent bleach to clear the hands. Cut two tomatoes in half, remove the skins, wash the hands with the pulp. Leave on for 5–10 minutes, then wash off with rosewater with a few drops of simple tincture of benzoin added.

5) Soaking the hands daily in warm milk with a little

freshly squeezed lemon juice will soften the hands, and prevent dryness and wrinkles.

6)   After washing the hands, always dry them thoroughly, as half-dried hands result in roughness and chaps in the winter, and hard, dry skin in the summer.

7)   Keep a bottle of hand lotion or cream by the sink, so you can use it straight after the hands have been in water, when they are at their driest.

8)   In the summer, when the hands are hot and the palms sweaty, wash and dry them, then dust the palms with a little fine oatmeal.

9)   Always protect the hands in winter by wearing gloves, and massage the knuckles with warm olive oil.

10)   When using oils or hand creams in the winter, it is best to apply them warm. Heat gently in a cup standing in a pan of hot water.

Nails

Keeping the fingernails in good condition, beautifully shaped and intact, demands care and attention, but is well worth the trouble. There is nothing more unattractive than badly bitten nails, or nail varnish that has been left on too long, to become cracked and chipped.

If you have brittle nails file, never cut, them. It is best not to grow them too long, as the longer the nail, the weaker it is, and it is likely to split and break.

You can tell by looking at the nails if a person has a certain illness or disease. Ridges on the nails are a sure sign of poor health. When spots are found on several nails, it is a sign of the nervous system. When spots are due to injury, in time, as the nail grows, the spot will grow out. Very brittle nails are said to be a sign of gout.

Smoking will eventually cause the nails to become yellowish in colour. If the nails are badly stained, there is nothing that you can do to correct this, but it has been proved that naturally yellowish nails are stronger than milky white ones.

The growth of the nails varies in different individuals. On young hands the growth is more rapid. Nails grow quicker in the summer than they do in the winter. The nails on the right hand grow faster than those on the left, and the nail on the second finger away from the thumb will grow quicker and stronger than any of the other nails: strange, but true.

Superstition has it that if a child is born with a full moon on the seventh finger counting from the little finger on the left hand, which is the first finger on the right hand, he or she will be blessed with seven years of good fortune, but, alas, will sup sorrow for the rest of his life. It is also said that the moons on the nails will turn blue as the owner approaches death. When death is imminent, they will become black.

Do you ever stop to think what day it is when you cut your nails? This is a very old poem, that my grandmother can remember her aunt saying:

CUTTING THE NAILS
Cut them on Monday, cut them for news,
Cut them on Tuesday, for a new pair of shoes,
Cut them on Wednesday, cut for a letter,
Cut them on Thursday, for something better,
Cut them on Friday, cut them for sorrow,

Cut them on Saturday, to see your sweetheart tomorrow,
Cut them on Sunday, your safety go seek,
For Satan will have you for the rest of the week!

FOR A PERFECT MANICURE

To keep your nails in good condition, give yourself a professional manicure each week. It is easy, and a lot cheaper once you know how. Follow the section below: you can't go wrong, it's so simple.

1) Remove all traces of old nail varnish, using an oily varnish remover.

2) Soak the hands in warm, soapy water, to soften the cuticles at the base of the nails.

3) Attend to the cuticles first. Dip an orange stick into soapy water and gently push back the skin. Work around the base of each nail so that it is quite loose. Never cut the base of the nails, as it will cause 'hang nails', which are very painful.

4) Dip the fingers into warm water, then rub with a soft towel.

5) Gently massage a little almond or olive oil into each nail, pushing back the skin at the base of the nail as you do so.

6) Shape the nails with the rough side of an emery board. When filing, always file the nails upwards towards the centre of the nail. Never file outwards. Once you have filed the nails into shape, use the softer side of the emery board very lightly.

7) Before applying nail varnish, apply a base coat, which will prevent the nails from staining and provides a smooth surface for the varnish.

8) If your nails split and break easily, apply a strengthener to dry nails before the base coat.

9) Always apply nail varnish in three strokes, along the length of each nail. Allow to dry for 5 minutes, then apply the second coat. On the second coat, finish by taking the colour around the tip of the nails to seal it.

10) For a clear, long-lasting finish, apply a top coat over the dry nail varnish, brushing it in three even, long strokes along the length of each nail.

TIPS FOR NAILS

1) Remove all nail varnish at least once a week, using an oily remover.

2) To strengthen the nails, eat one cube of clear white jelly daily.

3) To remove stains from the nails, wash and dry the hands, then apply fresh lemon juice to the nails with cotton wool.

4) If the nails are brittle, soak the hands in warm soapy water for three minutes each night. Dry the hands, then gently massage a little almond or olive oil into the fingernails.

5) Long fingernails look great in deep colours like Morello, Moody Mauve or deep blood red.

6) If you have short nails, keep to the softer paler shades like Iced Pink, Pearl Peach and Koral.

7) Long, pointed nails will add to the hands, and make the fingers look longer and thinner.

8) To keep long nails at their best and in tip-top condition, massage and file them gently every day, using the softer side of the emery board.

Toenails and Feet

If you wear open-toed shoes in the summer, you probably paint your toenails the same colour as your fingernails. But do you take the same amount of time and care over your toenails as you do over your fingernails? If you don't, then follow this section carefully, as looking after the toenails is just as important. If care is not taken, it could lead to in-growing toenails, which are very painful and have to be removed.

Trim the toenails every week, but don't cut them too short or they will be painful. Below are some helpful tips on cutting toenails.

TIPS FOR CUTTING TOENAILS
1)   Before you cut the nails, soak the feet in a foot bath. Add a tablespoon of oil of lavender, oil of sweet almonds or oil of jasmine to warm water. Soak the feet for 10 minutes.
2)   Dry the feet with a soft warm towel, then massage the whole foot with a body lotion, massaging gently into the skin around the toe nails. Dust over the feet with a little talcum powder.
3)   Cut the nails straight across, then smooth away the sharp corners with the softer side of an emery board.

TIPS FOR FEET AND NAILS
1)   Always soak the feet before cutting the nails.
2)   Always cut the nails straight across, then file the corners.
3)   Massage the skin around the nails every night with a little body lotion.

4)   If a toe nail is split, never pull off: cut across the split, then file smooth with an emery board.

5)   To keep the feet supple, walk around the house barefoot for 15–20 minutes daily.

6)   Bathe the feet daily in warm water with one tablespoon of witch hazel added.

7)   After bathing the feet, massage the soles, instep and ankles with a good after-bath lotion. Finish by dusting the feet with a little talcum powder.

8)   If you suffer from hot, perspiring feet, bathe them daily in warm water with three tablespoons of common salt added. After drying, massage the feet with a little witch hazel, dust the soles of the feet with talc and sprinkle a little talc into your shoes.

9)   There is no actual cure for flat feet once the instep arch has given way. Wear a support, and try the exercises below: they might help to bring relief, and, if the problem is caught in the early stages, help to prevent it from developing further.

EXERCISES TO DO DAILY FOR FLAT FEET

1)   Stretch the leg out straight. Bend it at the ankle, bending the toes backwards.

2)   Without moving the foot, bend the toes downwards.

3)   Keeping the toes bent downwards, stretch out the foot, making the ankle rigid.

4)   While keeping the ankle rigid, bend the toes upwards.

5)   Relax the feet, and gently massage them with a little olive oil.

   Do not carry out these exercises if you feel any pain, or if you have back trouble or any other muscular complaint.

3 Natural Perfumes, Scented Baths & Pot-Pourris

PERFUMES

Selecting perfume is very much an individual choice. Some prefer a heavy, strong, oriental perfume; others a light, delicate, fresh fragrance, like 'Ashes of Roses', or 'Lily of the Valley'.

The type of perfume that a woman wears says a lot about her personality, life-style and career. A businesswoman, who knows what she wants, who is independent and ambitious, may choose a powerful, classic perfume to match her make-up and clothes. The 'girl next door', young, sweet and pretty, but rather shy, may prefer a light, soft, feminine perfume: enough to give a hint of appeal, but not enough to attract attention to herself. And what about the 'vamp'? I am sure that everyone knows a woman like this: she is the woman we all love to hate. She loves to be the centre of attention and to stand out in a crowd. She is a flirt and likes to be noticed, particularly by men. She will choose a strong, heavy perfume, that is both classy and expensive.

Great-aunt will want a perfume to remind her of her youth, when all the girls smelt of sweet rose, lavender or eau-de-Cologne.

You will find that the most important ingredient in nearly all home-made perfumes is oil of rose. Rose oil is the most useful and valuable of all the natural perfume oils. It takes approximately 30 roses to make one drop of oil; it is usually made from the Damask Rose, which has a very strong scent.

The roses are grown near Grasse in France, and they are always hand-picked at night, when their fragrance is at its strongest.

Making your own perfume is very rewarding.

I have listed a few of my favourites, which I hope will encourage you to make your own. Whatever scent you prefer, I am sure that you will find one here that you will particularly like.

BERGAMOT AND ROSE PERFUME

This is a delightful perfume, and a few drops added to the washing water will sweetly scent your clothes.

24 tablespoons surgical spirits	1 teaspoon oil of lavender
20 drops oil of bergamot	1 teaspoon oil of musk
10 drops oil of rose	

Pour the surgical spirits into a bottle and add the other ingredients in the order in which they are listed above. Shake well after each addition.

EAU-DE-COLOGNE

This scent has a nice fresh smell. When I was a child, there was always a bottle of eau-de-Cologne on my grandmother's dresser. Not only did she use it as a perfume, but also to bring relief from a headache by applying a little to the forehead.

2 tablespoons fresh rose petals

2 tablespoons grated orange peel

1 tablespoon fresh basil leaves

1 tablespoon mint leaves

2 tablespoons eau-de-Cologne

1 cup vodka

2 cups boiling water

Soak the rose petals in the vodka for one week, in a screw-topped jar.

Dry the basil and mint leaves in a warm but airy place, out of direct sunlight. When the leaves are ready, they will be crisp and crumble between the fingers when rubbed together: if not, leave to dry for a few more days.

When dry, crush the basil and mint leaves and put into an earthenware jug.

Add the grated orange peel and pour over the boiling water.

Add the 2 tablespoons of eau-de-Cologne and stir. Cover the jug and leave to steep.

When the infusion is cool, strain.

Strain the rose and vodka infusion and pour the two liquids together into a glass bottle. Shake well.

JASMINE AND LAVENDER PERFUME

The sweet smell of jasmine together with the strong scent of the lavender makes this a lovely perfume.

dried jasmine flowers	2 pints white wine
dried lavender flowers	vinegar
dried rose petals	½ pint rosewater

Dry a good quantity of jasmine and lavender flowers and rose petals.

To every 4 oz (8 tablespoons) of jasmine and lavender flowers, mixed, add 2 oz (2 tablespoons) of rose petals.

Mix together and put into a large screw-topped jar.

Pour over the white wine vinegar and shake well. Add the rosewater and shake again.

Leave to stand for 10 days before straining, then bottle.

LAVENDER WATER

This makes a refreshing toilet water. It is also a good remedy for a headache: a hanky soaked in it and wrung out, then laid across the forehead, will soon bring relief.

16 tablespoons dried lavender, flowers and tops	½ pint rosewater
1 pint cider vinegar	

Put the lavender flowers and tops into a screw-topped jar.

Pour over the cider vinegar and leave to infuse for 1 week in a cool, dark place. Shake daily.

After 1 week, strain the lavender infusion through a sieve lined with muslin.

Pour the rosewater into the infusion, stirring well, then bottle.

Shake before use; use as required.

ROSE WATER

Rose water can be bought, but if you have a rose garden you can make your own. As well as being a light perfume and an ingredient in many of the recipes in this book, it is also a useful lotion for sun burn.

　　6 cups fresh rose petals (any
　　　　fragrant variety)
　　1¾ pints fresh rain water

Put the rose petals into a deep ovenproof dish and cover with the rain water.

Put into a hot oven, gas mark 6, and leave for one hour.

When cool, strain and bottle.

This will keep for up to four days.

SCENT CAKES

These scent cakes are easy to make and smell delightful.
You can put them in the wardrobe or drawers to perfume
your clothes; or into cupboards, or even your handbag, to
perfume the contents.

½ lb lump paraffin
2 tablespoons oil of verbena

2 teaspoons oil of cloves
2 teaspoons oil of
  lavender

Gently melt the paraffin and stir in the oils in the order in
which they are listed above.
Pour into a shallow tin to set.
When hard, cut into shapes.
Or, I find it easier to place pretty-shaped pastry cutters onto
a biscuit tin lid and pour the liquid into the shapes to set.
When it hardens, you not only have pretty shapes, but they
are also a lot easier to remove from the cutters.

VIOLET PERFUME

1 dessertspoon essence of
  violets

½ pint water

Boil the water, then leave until it is tepid.
Add the essence of violets and quickly bottle, so that the oil
doesn't lose any of its fragrance. Shake well to blend
together thoroughly.

Apply to the skin with a sponge, allowing the scent to sink into the skin. The perfume will last up to 24 hours when applied this way.

Any other perfume or oil can be added to the essence of violets to give a stronger scent, before adding the oil to the water. Oil of rose is nice added to the violet oil, but, for a stronger scent, I find that a few drops of Devonshire Violet perfume give a strong, sweet smell, and also give the perfume colour.

Perfumed Sachets

You can use freshly-picked herbs to fill a sachet, but after 3 or 4 weeks they will have lost their scent, so it is best to use them dried. The scent lasts longer, and after 6 months, when the herbs are losing their smell, you can add a few drops of oil to the cotton sachet to bring out the fragrance. For drying herbs see *Drying and Storing Herbs*, p. 137.

Come September I am forever sewing, making sachets and pot-pouri for Christmas presents. A basket filled with sweet smelling pot pourri with a pretty sachet filled with the same on top makes a lovely gift, and they are always in demand. (See p. 101 to make your own pot-pourri.)

LAVENDER SACHET

Pick a large handful of lavender. Tie the bottom of the stalks with ribbon, and hang in the wardrobe to dry for 5 to 6 weeks.

When the lavender is dry, remove from the stalks by running your fingers up the stalks. Put into an airtight container to maintain its smell.

Make attractive sachets in square, round or heart shapes from thin cotton, trimmed around the edge with lace. Fill with the lavender. Sew on a loop if it is to hang in the wardrobe.

LEMON AND ORANGE SACHET

Place in the wardrobe, cupboard or drawers, to keep your clothes smelling sweet all the year round.

1 pint lemon verbena leaves
4 tablespoons lemon peel

4 tablespoons powdered orange
a few drops oil of verbena or fresh lemon juice

Put the dried lemon verbena leaves into an airtight plastic container. Add the grated lemon peel, then sprinkle over the powdered orange and shake well.

Add the oil of verbena or fresh lemon juice.

Sew into sachets.

ROSE SACHET

6 cups of red rose petals
6 drops oil of rose
1 teaspoon mint leaves
1 teaspoon ground cloves

1 teaspoon ground
cinnamon
1 teaspoon ground
allspice
3 teaspoons orris-root
powder

Put the dried rose petals and the dried mint leaves into an airtight plastic container. Sprinkle over the ground cloves, cinnamon, allspice and orris-root powder, shaking well after each addition.
Sprinkle over the oil of rose and mix well.
Sew into sachets, or use to refill old pomanders.

SCENTED BATHS

There is nothing more refreshing and relaxing than a sweet-smelling herbal bath, to ease and soothe away aches and pains. Bath vinegars are invigorating and also act as antiseptics. Oatmeal is used to soften the water and herbs to scent it, releasing their natural oils to soothe and soften the skin. A herbal bath will help to aid sleep, and the vapour from the oils will cleanse the skin.

Lavender has been used for thousands of years, not only for its sweet, strong fragrance, but also for its soothing qualities. Practically any herb can be used with lavender: rosemary, thyme, lemon balm or mint.

Here are just a few of my favourites. If I had to choose one, it would be the Violet Bath Oil, as it is one of my own remedies, which I am pleased to share with you. If you like a stronger scent, add a few drops of Devonshire Violet perfume to the bath water, before adding the violet bath oil.

BASIL BATH VINEGAR

Basil is a powerful herb of great importance to herb lovers. It was brought to Europe by monks, and came to England in 1548.

½ pint cider vinegar   3 tablespoons basil
½ pint soft water   leaves, fresh or dried

Mix together the vinegar and water and heat until almost boiling.
Add the basil leaves, cover the pan and leave to steep overnight.
Strain, and bottle.
To use: add ½ pint to a bath. It is both relaxing and refreshing, and also acts as an antiseptic.

MINT BATH VINEGAR

This bath vinegar is refreshing and acts as an antiseptic. It is particularly beneficial if you are feeling a bit under the weather.

3 tablespoons dried mint   ½ pint cider vinegar
  leaves   ½ pint soft water
1 tablespoon dried
  marjoram leaves
1 tablespoon dried lemon
  balm leaves

Bring the vinegar and the water to the boil.
Add all the herbs, remove from heat and cover with a saucer. Leave to steep for 8 hours.
Strain into a bottle or screw-topped jar and shake well.
Add one cupful to a bath.

GERANIUM AND LAVENDER BATH SALTS

2 lb sodium bicarbonate
4 tablespoons oil of
geranium

2 tablespoons oil of
lavender

Mix the oils together, bottle and shake thoroughly.

Take a large glass jar with a well-fitted lid and a wide mouth and put a layer of sodium bicarbonate into the jar, about 2 inches deep. Sprinkle over one tablespoon of the mixed oils. Repeat these layers until the jar is full.

Shake well and leave for 2 to 3 weeks before using.

Add 2 to 3 tablespoons to each bath.

JUNIPER BATH OIL

The sweet smell of juniper makes this bath oil both refreshing and relaxing.

10 drops essential oil of
juniper
10 drops rosemary oil
10 drops oil of pine

2 tablespoons almond oil
4 tablespoons mild
washing-up liquid

Pour all the oils into an airtight plastic container, so that the fragrance does not escape and shake well.

Pour the oils into a jar and cover with a saucer. Place the jar in about 2 inches of water in a pan and simmer for one hour.

Add the washing-up liquid to the oils and beat well.

Remove from heat and bottle.

Shake well before using, one or two tablespoons to a bath.

VIOLET BATH OIL

1 cup violet flowers, freshly
  picked or dried
10 drops oil of violets
10 drops oil of lavender

6 drops oil of rose
4 tablespoons mild
  washing-up liquid,
  unscented if possible

Put the violet flowers into an earthenware or china jug.
Pour over ½ pint of boiling water, cover with a plate or
saucer and leave for 3 hours.
Strain, and add the oil of violets to the violet water.
Add the other oils and put into an earthenware jug. Stand
the jug in about 2 inches of water in a pan, cover the jar so
that the oils' vapours don't escape and simmer for 1 hour.
Add the washing-up liquid to the oils and beat well.
Remove from the heat and bottle.
Shake well before using, one or two tablespoons to a bath.

ROSE BATH TABLETS

6 drops oil of rose
8 tablespoons bicarbonate
  of soda
2 tablespoons orris-root
  powder

1½ teaspoons tartaric
  acid
1 teaspoon lemon juice
surgical spirits

Mix together the bicarbonate of soda and the tartaric acid.
Add the lemon juice and the oil of rose to the orris-root
powder and stir in well.

Add the mixed soda and acid to the orris-root powder and mix to a stiff paste with a little surgical spirits.

Divide into squares about an inch thick and place on a baking tray to dry.

Store in a glass jar. Two tablets will soften and scent the bath water.

ROSE BATH WATER

10 drops essence of rose
5 tablespoons rosewater
20 drops oil of bergamot

1 teaspoon lavender oil
24 tablespoons surgical spirits

Pour all the oils into a glass bottle, add the rosewater and the surgical spirits and shake well to blend the oils thoroughly.

Add a few drops to the bath water to give a light, sweet smell.

Bath Bags

TO MAKE A BATH BAG
You will need a piece of butter muslin, about 4 inches square, or 6 inches if you are to fill with extra herbs. Sew two squares together, leaving an opening to fill with the herbs. Once the bag is filled, gather the top and tie, making a loop to hang onto the taps. If you can't get butter muslin, cotton will work just as well.

SAGE AND LAVENDER BATH

2 tablespoons dried sage
  leaves
1 dessertspoon dried
  lavender tops

dried orange peel
butter muslin

Into a bag made from butter muslin, put the sage leaves and lavender tops and the peel of half an orange, shredded.

Put the bag into a glass jug or bowl filled with ½ pint of boiling water, cover with a plate and leave to soak for 15 minutes.

Squeeze out the bag into the boiling water, bottle and shake well.

Add all the liquid to the bath water.

BRAN AND LEMON BATH

To soften and purify the skin and to reduce enlarged pores.

3 tablespoons bran
1 tablespoon dried
  shredded lemon peel

butter muslin

Put the bran and lemon peel into a bag of butter muslin.

Place the bag in a glass jug of boiling water, cover with a plate and allow to soak for 15 minutes.

Squeeze out the bag into the water in which it has been steeped and bottle.

Add all the liquid to the bath water.

LAVENDER BATH BAG

1 small cup lavender tops
  and stalks
6 tablespoons oatmeal

3 tablespoons almond
  meal

Mix all the ingredients together and put into a butter muslin or cotton bag.

Hang the bag onto the hot tap and let the water run through. Afterwards the bag may be used to wash yourself, but mind that you don't scratch yourself with the sharp lavender stalks. Lasts for three baths.

YARROW AND LAVENDER BATH BAG

½ cup yarrow leaves
½ cup lavender, flowers and
  tops

½ cup rosemary leaves
2 handfuls oatmeal

Mix all the ingredients together in a bowl, then put into a muslin bag.

Hang on the hot tap, and allow the water to run through. It will last up to three baths.

Yarrow can be found growing in hedgerows or on waste ground. It has been used for hundreds of years by country folk. It is a good all-round herb, used to treat conditions from a common cold to an oily complexion. However, this useful herb will creep its way into gardens and though it is loved by many, it is a nightmare to proud gardeners.

HYSSOP BATH BAG

2 tablespoons dried hyssop | 1 tablespoon porridge
1 tablespoon dried lavender | 1 tablespoon Marvel

Mix all the ingredients together in a bowl, then put into a muslin or cotton bag.

Hang on the hot tap, and let the full force of the water run through the bag. This will last up to three baths. Use the bag to rub over your body, to clean, soften and nourish the skin.

OATMEAL BATH BAG

To soften the skin and perfume the water.

10 tablespoons fine oatmeal | 1 tablespoon
2 tablespoons orris-root | almondmeal
   powder

Mix all the ingredients together in a bowl and put the mixture into a muslin bag.

Tie the bag onto the hot tap and allow the water to run through it, then squeeze it into the bath. Use the bag to wash with. The orris-root powder gives it a faint smell of violets and a few drops of oil of violet can be added to give a stronger scent.

When using bath bags, don't have the water too hot, as a warm bath is more relaxing.

When using oils, it is best to close windows, so that the vapours from the oils don't escape.

POT POURRI

The name 'pot-pourri' literally means 'rot pot'. For hundreds of years petals and all kinds of herbs have been rotted down in pots into a damp gooey mess and covered with a perforated lid to give off scent, to counteract the evil smell of the days before modern sanitation.

There are two kinds of pot-pourri: one is dry and the other moist. As everybody has a different sense of smell and individual taste varies, you can vary the basic ingredients to make over a hundred different pot-pourris. Old pot-pourri bowls can sometimes be bought in antique shops. Some old recipes require gum benzoin and angelica root, both of which are hard to obtain, but most of the other ingredients can be bought from a good chemist, health shop or herbalist. I give a list of suppliers at the back of the book.

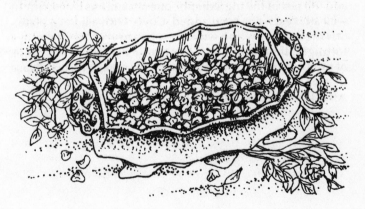

A QUEEN ELIZABETH I RECIPE FOR A MOIST
POT POURRI

This pot-pourri dates back as far as 1565. It is sweet smelling and moist.

½ gallon fresh rose petals, any scented variety
6 tablespoons table salt
4 tablespoons finely rubbed bay salt
4 tablespoons ground allspice
4 tablespoons ground cloves
4 tablespoons brown sugar
¼ oz gum benzoin
4 tablespoons orris-root powder
1 dessertspoonful brandy
8 tablespoons lavender flowers
8 tablespoons lemon verbena leaves
4 tablespoons geranium leaves

Put all the rose petals into a container, sprinkle over the table and bay salts and leave for three days.

Put the petals into a large earthenware or china bowl and add the rest of the ingredients, one at a time as listed. Stir in well after each has been added. Cover with a lid or a plate.

Stir the mixture with a wooden spoon every three days for a fortnight. If the mixture seems a little dry, add a few drops of brandy, for if a moist pot-pourri becomes dry, it will lose its scent.

After three weeks, it is ready to put into pots.

A QUEEN ELIZABETH I RECIPE FOR A DRY POT POURRI

The mixture of thyme, lavender and rosemary makes this a lovely dry, sweet-smelling pot-pourri.

1 cup red, scented rose petals, dried
1 cup dried rosemary, lavender and lemon thyme, mixed
dried grated peel of 1 orange
dried grated peel of 1 lemon
1 teaspoon ground allspice
½ tablespoon ground cloves
6 dried bay leaves
½ teaspoon orris-root powder

Put all the dried rose petals and herbs into an air-tight container, sprinkle over the dried grated orange and lemon peel, shake well, then leave for 24 hours.

Lightly pound the ground allspice, ground cloves and dried bay leaves with a rolling pin and add to the mixture.

Sprinkle over the orris-root powder, shaking well to retain the perfume.

Keep the pot-pourri in the container in a dark cupboard for one week, gently stirring the mixture daily with your hand, after which it will be ready to put into pots.

For drying herbs see *Drying and Storing Herbs*, p. 137.

GERANIUM POT POURRI

2 cups dried geranium
  leaves
1 cup dried lavender
1 cup dried red rose petals

1 tablespoon orris-root
  powder
1 crushed cinnamon stick

Rub the dried geranium leaves gently to bring out the scent and put into an air-tight container with the rose petals and lavender.

Add the crushed cinnamon to the orris-root powder, and sprinkle over the herbs a little at a time.

Screw the lid on tightly, shake, then leave for two to three days in a dark place. Shake gently daily, to cover all the herbs with the sweet smelling orris-root.

Put into an earthenware or china bowl and place in the room to scent.

GOLDEN POT POURRI

1 cup dried lemon verbena
  leaves
1 cup lemon balm leaves
1 cup chamomile flowers
½ cup marigold petals,
  orange and yellow mixed

dried peel of 1 lemon
a few drops lemon juice,
  fresh or bottled
½ cup orris-root powder

Put all the dried herbs, leaves and petals into an air-tight plastic container or a glass screw-topped jar and mix around with your hand to bring out the scent.

Cut up the dried lemon peel and add to the mixture.

Add a few drops of the lemon juice and shake well.

Sprinkle over the orris-root a little at a time, shaking well as you do so.

Put the pot-pourri into pots or bowls.

If placed in the kitchen, this pot-pourri will take away any unpleasant smells when cooking. The mixture of orange and yellow marigolds with white chamomile flowers and the sweet smell of lemon verbena and lemon balm makes this an excellent pot-pourri, ideal for the kitchen, bathroom or bedroom.

MARIGOLD AND MINT POT POURRI

This pot-pourri has rather a nice smell.

1 cup marigold flowers, orange and yellow mixed
½ cup dried peppermint leaves
½ cup dried thyme leaves

4 drops oil of peppermint
½ cup orris-root powder

Lightly crush the marigold flowers together with the dried herbs before putting into a plastic air-tight container or a screw-topped glass jar.

Add the orris-root powder a little at a time, shaking well.

Sprinkle over the peppermint oil and gently mix around with your hand.

Put into a dark cupboard for one day, shaking every few hours.

Put into pots or bowls.

MY MOTHER'S SWEET POT POURRI

Collect and dry different herbs and flowers throughout the year. Keep the mixture in a plastic air-tight container: a screw-topped plastic shop sweet jar is ideal. Keep on adding to the mixture, and by the winter the mixture will be sweet smelling, colourful and ready to use. Always dry the herbs, leaves, or flowers before adding to the mixture.

Start off by drying rose petals and rose buds in May–June, with lilacs, wallflowers, mock oranges, honeysuckle, lime, meadowsweet, pinks, borage, marigolds and violets: in fact, any flower that is colourful or scented. Put all together in the container, and sprinkle over one or two tablespoons of orris-root powder, shaking well.

During July, add the leaves of mint, peppermint, thyme, lemon balm, lemon verbena, marjoram and rosemary. Dry before adding. Also add dried, grated lemon and orange peel, a pinch of ground allspice and ground cloves. Gently stir the mixture around with your hand. Sprinkle over a little more orris-root and shake well daily. Keep in a dark cupboard. Use your sense of smell: if it doesn't smell sweet enough, then add a little more orris-root. Add extra pretty flowers: not for scent, but for colour.

In September, put into pots and place in different rooms.

ROSE POT POURRI

This is a sweet smelling pot-pourri, and one of my favourites. It is best to use red roses: Damask Rose and Fragrant Cloud are two nice, strong roses to use, along with any other coloured roses for scent and for colour. Once you have started your pot-pourri, you can keep adding to it, to improve the colour and scent. Lavender, rosemary and violets blend in well with this pot-pourri.

6 cups dried rose petals and a handful of rosebuds
½ cup lemon verbena leaves, marigold petals and common daisy, mixture
1 teaspoon dried mint leaves
1 teaspoon ground cloves
1 teaspoon ground cinnamon
1 teaspoon ground allspice
3 teaspoons orris-root powder
6 drops oil of rose

Put all the dried herbs and flowers into a plastic container and mix together with your hand.
Sprinkle over the orris-root powder a little at a time, shaking well.
Sprinkle over the ground spices in the order listed above, shaking after each addition.
Sprinkle over the oil of rose and give a final shake.
Screw the lid on tightly and leave overnight in a dark cupboard.
Put into pots or bowls.

SUMMER SWEET POT POURRI

4 cups rose petals
1 large cup lavender flowers, rosemary leaves, pinks, summer jasmine, honeysuckle flowers, dried and mixed
3 dried crushed sage leaves
1 dried sprig of parsley
1 dried sprig of thyme
2 handfuls table salt
½ tablespoon ground cinnamon
½ tablespoon ground cloves
½ tablespoon ground nutmeg
½ tablespoon ground allspice
4 tablespoons orris-root powder
juice and dried grated peel of 2 lemons
1 tablespoon oil of lavender
1 teaspoon oil of bergamot
1 teaspoon oil of geranium

This is a dry and a moist pot-pourri. It is a little expensive to make, unless you have a good collection of ground herbs and spices and a good store of oils.

First put the rose petals into an air-tight container and cover with the salt. Shake well, then leave in a dark cupboard for 1 week.

Add the dried lavender flowers, rosemary leaves, pinks, jasmine and honeysuckle flowers, the crushed sage leaves and the dried sprigs of parsley and thyme and screw the lid back on tightly, shaking well.

In another container, earthenware pot or china bowl mix together the four ground spices with the orris-root powder and stir into the rose petal mixture.

Add the lemon peel and the juice, a drop at a time.

Add the lavender, bergamot and geranium oils, sprinkling over a little at a time and stir well. Place in a dark cupboard for 24 hours. Put into pots.

THYME AND MARIGOLD POT POURRI

½ cup dried thyme leaves
½ cup dried marigold petals
½ cup peppermint leaves

½ cup dried basil leaves
½ cup orris-root powder
4 drops oil of thyme

Crush all the dried herbs and flowers together and put into an air-tight container.

Add the oil of thyme and mix well.

Sprinkle over the orris-root powder a little at a time, each time shaking the mixture gently.

Put into pots.

FLOWERS FOR POT-POURRI

The main ingredient for a beautiful pot-pourri is the rose petals, and the Damask Rose is the most fragrant. But all roses are beautiful, and there are many different varieties that have a strong scent.

These are a few of my favourites. I grow them in my garden, where I planted them for their scent.

Alec Red   bright crimson, with a very strong scent.

Blue Moon   full shaped, ice blue rose, strong scented.

Embassy Regal   cream overlaid peach pink rose, with a large flower of 30 petals, strong scent.

Fragrant Cloud   large coral red flower, very sweet and fragrant.

Lilac Rose   This rose carries three or four blooms on one stem. Beautiful, pastel shades of pink and lilac, with a delightful sweet scent.

Wendy Cussons   an old favourite, reddish pink in colour, with a sweet scent.

Whisky Mac   attractive rose, deep golden bronze in colour. Very strong scent.

I use these for the basis of all my pot-pourris. Every rose is beautiful, but not all have a fragrant smell; but you can still use all rose petals, and add rose oil, which you can buy at good garden centres or health shops, for scent.

Always store oils in a dark place, away from heat and direct sunlight. It is best not to stock up with oils, as they tend to evaporate.

If you haven't got your own garden, then look out for rose petals wherever you go or in parks, or garden centres, or ask friendly neighbours. Always carry a bag with you in which to collect them. Never pick petals off the rose while it is still on the stem: use only the petals that have fallen off the rose to the ground.

These roses are also good to use for their scent and colour.

Bristol Post   this rose has no fragrance, but is full of colour, carrying large flowers in shades of salmon, pink and golden orange.

Fred Fairbrother   a well shaped crown, deep scarlet in the bud, opening to a bright cerise. Very strong scent.

Maritime Bristol   a beautiful rose, pure tangerine in colour, with deep green leaves and a delicate freesia-like fragrance.

Mischief   an excellent garden rose. Attractive deep salmon colour. Very fragrant.

Prima Ballerina   very strong scented rose, with deep green leaves and high pointed flowers of clear deep pink.

Sugar Sweet   1974 winner of the Henry Edland Memorial

Medal for the most fragrant rose on trial. A bright cherry pink colour in the bud, opening to a golden base. A very beautiful rose, both in colour and fragrance.

Zepherine Drouhin   silver pink in colour. This is a climbing rose, which is thornless and sweetly scented.

Zola   a shrub rose with light green leaves and golden petals. Richly fragrant.

When you have finished your pot-pourri and it is all dried and sweet smelling, add a few extra bright-coloured flowers to it for appearance. I have found that the best flowers to dry and add to the pot-pourri are the following:

Borage   one of my favourite herbs, which has a lovely blue flower.

Cornflowers   original blue and mixed colours; pinks, white and lilac.

Dianthus   commonly known as 'pinks.' Use all colours.

Helichrysum   everlasting flowers, also used in winter flower arrangements.

Lobelia   white, pink, and blue flowers.

Viola   beautiful 'Jersey Gem', a lovely blue flower.

Violets   delightful little flower, deep purple in colour. One of my favourite flowers, it dries perfectly.

If I listed all the flowers that I dry and use, it would be endless. Any flower which is brightly coloured can be dried and added to the pot-pourri, to make it look more attractive.

When it is a hard winter, cold and snowing, smelling your pot-pourri when you walk into the room, and seeing the beautiful dried flowers, which will still have their natural, pretty colours, will bring a little summer into the house.

4 *Traditional recipes for health & beauty*

HERBAL TEAS & HEALTH DRINKS

There are many herb books that deal with herbal teas in a more serious and detailed manner than I am able to here, and offer recipes for different teas. I have chosen those listed here mainly for their cleansing qualities, but I also mention their medicinal uses. You can enjoy these teas as beauty beverages or for their medicinal properties, or simply drink them for pleasure. Some you will find delightful and will want to take often, others are not quite so pleasant.

You can make a tea from any herb, by allowing the dried flowers or leaves to steep in boiling water for a few minutes. If you like a strong tea, use more of the dried herb and allow to steep longer, but not for too long, as steeping will make the tea bitter. Experiment with other herbs, and discover new and different flavours. Honey and lemon can be added to sweeten woody teas, like nettle or dandelion; or add a pinch of ground cloves, nutmeg or cinnamon to give the tea a 'kick'. Never add milk to herbal teas: it will curdle, and mask the flavour of the herb.

BIRCH TEA

This tea should be made from fresh young leaves, which are full of vitamin C. It is a good tonic to clean out the system, and excellent to cure a spotty or dull complexion.

1 teaspoon fresh or dried birch leaves	½ pint boiling water

Put the birch leaves into an earthenware jug or teapot, and pour over the boiling water. Allow to stand for 8 minutes, then strain.
Take three times a day. This is pleasant to drink, if a bit woody. To sweeten, add a little honey or a few drops of lemon juice.

Medicinal use

The distilled water from the leaves will break down stones in the bladder or kidneys. It is also taken for gout and rheumatic complaints. The juice of the leaves will make a good mouth wash, to clear a sore throat.

CHAMOMILE TEA

This is a strong tea, somewhat unpleasant to taste, even with honey added, which can do nothing to improve the smell. Nevertheless it is a favourite, particularly in France, Germany and Switzerland.

1 tablespoon chamomile flowers, freshly picked	1 pint boiling water

Put the flowers into a teapot and pour over the pint of boiling water. Leave to stand for 5 to 6 minutes, then strain and sweeten to taste. Honey and lemon will improve the taste, a lump of sugar will also sweeten.
This tea is one of the most popular beauty beverages. For a clear smooth complexion, it should be taken last thing at night.

Medicinal use

This tea is taken for flatulence, digestive disorders and insomnia.

FENNEL TEA

Fennel is one of many anti-witch plants. It was grown in cottage gardens to protect the owner from enchantment. On midsummer's eve, country folk would gather the herb and hang it around the windows and doors to drive away witches and evil spirits. I have fennel growing in my garden, spreading along the front of my cottage, and, I must admit, I haven't so much as caught sight of a witch.

small handful fennel	½ pint boiling water

Put the fennel into a teapot or an earthenware jug, and pour over the boiling water. Allow to infuse for 5 minutes, then strain. Add a teaspoon of honey to sweeten. Take three times a day.

This pale green tea is light and pleasant tasting, with a strong smell of aniseed.

Medicinal use

When boiled in water and drunk, the leaves will soothe a sore stomach. Fennel seeds or roots help to open obstructions of the spleen and gall, and also the liver. The seeds will also help shortness of breath and wheezing. When drunk, fennel is good for colds, as it absorbs poisons in the body and fennel infusion is good for bathing sore eyes.

LEMON BALM TEA

1 teaspoon dried lemon balm leaves	1 teaspoon honey
½ pint boiling water	1 slice of lemon

Put the herb into a jug or teapot and cover with the boiling water. Leave to stand for 5 minutes, then strain. Add honey and lemon to taste. Take four cupfuls a day.

Do not be put off by the colour of this tea, which is a greenish-brown. The leaves give it a lovely lemon-scented smell, and the honey sweetens and adds to the taste. It is one of my favourite teas, pleasant to drink and excellent to clean out the stomach.

Culpeper said 'It causeth the mind and heart to become merry, and driveth away all troublesome cares and thoughts'.

Medicinal uses

This tea is excellent for vomiting and nausea, and will settle the stomach. It is particularly good for painful menstruation, as it eases cramp.

NETTLE TEA

The common stinging nettle, loved by few and hated by many, is a very useful herb. Nettle leaves are rich in minerals, and vitamins. This tea is generally a good all-round tonic.

2 teaspoons dried nettle leaves   ½ pint boiling water

Put the leaves into a teapot or an earthenware jug, pour over the boiling water, and leave to infuse for 8 minutes, then strain. Take as often as you like. To take away its woody taste, add honey and lemon.

Medicinal uses

When boiled, with honey and sugar added, the juice of the leaves is a safe medicine to open the passages to the lungs preventing shortness of breath and wheezing. When dried and burnt and inhaled through the mouth, the leaves will bring relief to asthma and bronchitis sufferers. Nettle juice is also a good gargle to help swelling of the mouth and throat. The leaves are mainly used for their diuretic properties and as an infusion they will relieve high blood pressure and cystitis. The leaves, rich in minerals, are a good tonic and blood purifier.

ORANGE FLOWER TEA

1 teaspoon dried orange flowers	½ pint boiling water

Pour the boiling water over the flowers and leave to stand for 6 minutes, then strain. Sweeten with honey if desired. Take one cupful three times a day before meals.

This tea is sweet to the taste, with a faint smell of cinnamon. The dried petals of the orange flowers make it a delightful tea to drink.

Medicinal uses

Orange flower tea acts as a mild nervine stimulant, and is a great tonic.

PARSLEY TEA

A little fresh parsley eaten daily will keep the eyes bright, and also sweeten the mouth and cure bad breath.

1 handful fresh common parsley, leaves and stalks	¾ pint soft water

Bring the water to the boil, pour over the parsley and leave to stand for 10 minutes, then strain. Add honey to sweeten if desired. Take 3 or 4 small cupfuls a day.

Medicinal uses

Parsley is full of iron and vitamins, aids digestion and relieves cramps in menstruation. When laid on the eyelids the leaves will bring relief to sore or swollen eyes. It will prevent wind, and cleanse the stomach and bowels. When boiled, the root can be eaten like a parsnip.

PRIMROSE TEA

Primrose tea is excellent to take if you are feeling hysterical, nervous, or restless and unable to sleep.

½ cup freshly picked primrose flowers	2 cups boiling water

Steep the primrose flowers in boiling water for 15 minutes before straining. Take as often as you like.

Medicinal uses

The juice of the root sniffed through the nose will help stop attacks of sneezing. A tablespoonful of the infusion will bring relief from a bad headache. Primrose has been used by country folk for hundreds of years to treat rheumatism and gout.

SAGE TEA

Sage flowers attract bees, which produce wonderful sage honey, which commands a high price. The tea is an excellent beauty beverage. It is pleasant to drink, and is a blood purifier.

SAGE TEA (My Grandmother's Remedy)

2 tablespoons dried sage leaves	orange juice
1 pint soft water	

Put the sage leaves into a teapot and cover with the boiling water. Allow to stand for 6 to 8 minutes, then strain and add a few drops of freshly squeezed orange juice to flavour. Take one small cupful three times a day, before or after meals.

SAGE TEA

1 cup fresh sage leaves
2 pints boiling water

2 tablespoons white
    sugar
juice of 1 lemon, freshly
    squeezed

Put all the ingredients into an earthenware jug and pour over the boiling water. Cover with a plate or saucer and leave to infuse for 30 minutes. Stir well for 1 minute, then strain. Take the tea warm, in small frequent doses.

Medicinal uses

Three spoonfuls of the juice with a little honey added taken when fasting will stop casting of the blood for those with consumption. When taken warm, the juice of the sage will help to clear a dry cough. Sage and vinegar were given to the plague victims to stop sweating. A soothing gargle can be made from sage, rosemary and honeysuckle boiled in wine or water, with alum or honey added. Sage, boiled with lavender, rosemary and mint, will make a comforting herbal bath, to help cold, tired joints, and to ease cramp. It is good for the digestion and for a weak stomach.

YARROW TEA

1 tablespoon dried yarrow
    leaves
1 pint boiling water

1 tablespoon honey

Put the herb into a teapot or an earthenware jug, pour over the boiling water and allow to infuse for 10 minutes, before straining and adding the honey to sweeten. Yarrow makes a strong tea. It should be taken warm, in small cupfuls, 2 or 3 times daily.

Medicinal uses

A poultice made from yarrow leaves and toadflax applied outwardly will induce sleep, ease pain and reduce bleeding. In Scotland, an ointment is still made from yarrow leaves and applied to open sores and ulcers. Yarrow contains cineol, which is a natural antiseptic. Country folk call it 'nosebleed', as it contains a substance which will clot blood, and it will reduce blood pressure, and heal bleeding piles. Yarrow purifies the blood, and the tea is excellent to take for a cold as it will open pores. It is also recommended for children in the early stages of a cold, and is good for measles.

BARLEY WATER

This is a pleasant drink, good for the stomach and excellent for a dry, blotchy skin, when taken regularly.

4 oz pearl barley	peel of ½ a fresh lemon
1 ¼ pints soft water	1 teaspoon clear honey

Wash the barley, put into a saucepan and cover with the water. Bring to the boil and simmer for 1 hour.
After it has simmered for half an hour, add the fresh lemon peel.

Strain while still hot, then leave to cool before bottling.
Store in the fridge in a bottle or jug and take three times a
day. A teaspoon of honey may be added to each glassful to
sweeten.

CABBAGE WATER

This drink is rich in iron, calcium, magnesium and
phosphorus and is a very good remedy for bad skin.

1 small fresh cabbage	lemon juice, bottled or
1 ½ mugs water	fresh

Wash the cabbage, shake off the drops and cut in half.
Put one half into a saucepan with the water and boil for 20
minutes.
Strain, and bottle the water
Put the other half of the cabbage into a liquidiser and
liquidise until you are left with a thinnish green liquid.
Add the bottled cabbage water and a few drops of lemon
juice and liquidise for a few seconds.
Drink straight away, while it is fresh. This will keep in the
fridge for a few days, but will lose some of its goodness
when stored.

CARROT JUICE

This drink is full of vitamin A and will cleanse the skin and strengthen the eyes.

3 large fresh carrots   soft water

Put the carrots into a pan, add enough water to cover and bring to the boil.
Remove from heat and cool.
Put the water and the carrots into a liquidiser and liquidise.
Drink the same day. Add a little tabasco to taste.

CELERY JUICE

This juice is an excellent diuretic, and is good to take before a period, when you feel bloated. It will also help slimmers to lose weight.

1 lb fresh celery   cayenne pepper
½ cup water

Wash the celery and chop into pieces.
Liquidise the chopped celery with the water, and a pinch of cayenne pepper to add taste.
Drink straight away when fresh. This will keep in the fridge for up to two days.

DANDELION TONIC

This is good for the skin and eyes, and will cleanse the liver.

1 large carefully removed	2 pints water
dandelion root	

Choose a young root by looking at the flowers and leaves: if the flowers are bright yellow and it has young, salad green, unmarked leaves, then the root itself is healthy. Be careful not to damage the root when removing from the earth. This will take time, about 2 hours, as dandelion roots grow deep into the ground. Allow it to dry naturally, for about two weeks.

When dry, boil in 2 pints of water, until the water is reduced to 1 pint, then strain and bottle.

Take 4 teaspoonfuls three times a day. Will keep up to 3 months.

ELDERBERRY ROB

This is my favourite health drink. I drink it cold from the fridge in the summer, and hot during the winter to prevent colds. This recipe dates back to 1773. Elder rob is full of vitamin C, and has a curative power of great repute. As a remedy it is taken hot at night to promote perspiration in the early stages of severe colds, and for symptoms such as shivering and sore throats. It is also taken for influenza, asthma and chest complaints. It is an excellent all-round tonic that I can highly recommend.

5 lb fresh elderberries   1 lb white sugar

Put the berries into a large saucepan, add a tablespoon of cold water and then stir in the sugar.

Simmer on a low heat until it is as thick as honey, stirring every few minutes.

Remove from the heat and strain through a sieve, using a wooden spoon to mash the berries. Sieve two or three times, then cool, bottle and store. Lasts up to 8 months.

To drink cold in the summer, add 2 tablespoons to a glass of water. I use bottled spring water.

To drink in the winter, add 2 tablespoons to a glass of hot water. If you are taking it for a cold, add a few drops of brandy, or, to sweeten, add a pinch of ground cloves or ground cinnamon.

Living in a 17th century cottage, I am surrounded by elder trees, so I pick as many berries as I can when ripe and make three to five bottles to store. It is best to use elderberries fresh, so look out for the elder tree when you are out walking in parks, fields or the countryside. Take a container and pick them. The best place to find an elder tree is in a graveyard.

PUMPKIN JUICE

This is full of vitamin A and potassium, and is an ideal pick-me-up when you're feeling low. It is also good to cleanse the skin, and for the stomach.

Liquidise the flesh of the pumpkin only, and then add bottled spring water.

Drink fresh the same day. It will keep in the fridge up to 3 days.

BEAUTY SLEEP

Sufficient sleep is essential for preserving the complexion, preventing wrinkles and keeping the eyes clear and bright. There may not be enough hours in the day to carry out a beauty routine, but there is no excuse at night. If you prepare your skin properly by removing make-up, and cleanse the face thoroughly, paying special attention to the grubby areas that attract dirt such as the chin, nose and forehead, your body will do the rest while you are asleep.

The amount of sleep that you need depends on your age and build and the amount of energy that you use up during the day, both physically and mentally. Anything from 4 to 8 hours sleep a night can be considered normal. If you sleep over 9 hours, the body begins to run down. The circulation of the blood will also slow down and become sluggish, and you may well wake up feeling tired and weak. You can lessen the amount of sleep that you need by adjusting your sleeping pattern: each day, get up 15 minutes earlier. Do this for two weeks, until you are spending less time in bed and asleep.

Many things that you do without thinking can and will affect your sleeping pattern. Going to bed after you have eaten a large meal is a bad idea. Apart from consuming a lot of calories that you will not burn off lying down, you will probably end up with indigestion. It is best to try not to drink tea, coffee, or alcohol before going to bed. Although alcohol will knock you out for a while, once it enters your blood stream it acts as a stimulant and will wake you up.

Insomnia, or sleeplessness, is another destroyer of beauty. Everyone has the odd sleepless night from time to time, then the sleep pattern is usually restored after a night or two. Sleeping difficulties often occur because we have broken the sleep patterns in some way. This could happen for a number of reasons, such as a crisis, which is a common cause of losing sleep, or because you are upset, worried, or tense. If sleeplessness continues for a long time after the upsetting event, the body will get used to the new habit, which then becomes difficult to correct. There is nothing more irritating than not being able to sleep, whatever the reason.

Snoring may be the subject of many a joke, but not for the partners who have to put up with it. There are many things that can cause snoring: lying flat on your back, sleeping with your mouth open, irritation from animal hair or feather pillows. A friend once came to me and asked for a remedy to stop her husband from snoring. I gave her many: sleep pillows, herbal bath bags, herbal drinks and more, but all failed, until I told her to give him one tablespoon of fresh, finely-chopped onion each night. That worked.

This section is full of useful tips to prevent sleepless nights: old and new remedies and cures for insomnia that I have collected together. Whatever problem may be causing your sleeplessness, I am sure that you will find a remedy here to help you.

Remedies for Insomnia

What better way to relax and unwind the body than to take

a sweet-smelling, soothing herbal bath? First set the scene. Dim the lights and have a little soft music in the background. Don't bathe in water that is too hot, as this can lead to broken capillaries and might cause you to faint. Have the water warm, between 98° and 100°F (36C–37C), which is very close to your body temperature.

There are many bath oils to choose from, the best of which for insomnia are:

Lavender   as it acts as a sedative

Sandalwood   for tranquillity

Jasmine   as it will relax and soothe the nerves.

Don't rub yourself hard after your bedtime bath: it will only wake you up again. Instead, gently pat yourself dry or, better still, slip into a warm, soft towelling robe, and let it absorb the moisture. Finish by gently rubbing yourself all over with a sweet-smelling body lotion. Lavender or violet are both sweet-smelling, and will leave your skin soft and smooth (See *Creams & Lotions for the Body*, p. 11).

COUNTRY CURE FOR INSOMNIA

A very old country remedy for insomnia is to eat one tablespoon of freshly-chopped raw onion before going to bed. Make sure that both you and your partner are taking this remedy. If not, eat a fresh sprig of parsley to sweeten the breath.

CURE FOR INSOMNIA

You can overcome insomnia by working on the solar plexus point, which is in the palm of your hand.

Press this point with your thumb for two minutes. Treat both hands. Use a little warm olive or almond oil.

DRINKS
A glass of warm milk with a teaspoon of clear honey added, sipped slowly, will aid sleep; or add one tablespoon of brandy instead of the honey: it will work just as well.

A syrup made from poppy seeds, which can be obtained from all good health shops, is an excellent remedy to help sleep.

Herbal teas such as chamomile, primrose, orange flower and yarrow, will induce sleep. (see *Herbal Teas & Health Drinks*, p. 112).

FOOD
Eating the right food can actually aid sleep, because the part of the nervous system that stimulates digestion also stimulates sleep relaxation. When you feel peckish before going to bed, try one of the following:

Parsley contains a gentle sedative, which has an aspirin-like effect.

Lettuce contains a relaxation-inducing chemical

Potato another good food to aid sleep.

Other foods which may aid sleep are: bananas, oatmeal and pomegranates.

POPPIES & HOPS
Poppies have a drugging effect. Pick them by the handful and place them all around the bedroom. They might give you a slight headache, but they will put you to sleep.

Hops are another good flower-herb to collect and put into the bedroom to help to aid sleep.

Sleep–inducing Pillows

A sleep pillow will soothe and relax the nerves, and induce sleep. Either pin the pillow to your bed pillow, so that the smell is inhaled directly, or put it in or under the pillow.

HOP SLEEP PILLOW

Pick a good bunch of fresh hops, tie the end of the stalks with string and hang up in a warm room to dry. When dry, remove from the stalk by running your thumb and first finger upwards. Make a small square sachet from muslin or thin cotton as for the perfumed sachets (see *Perfumed Sachets*, p. 90), fill with the hops and pin to your pillow.

HOPS AND LAVENDER SLEEP PILLOW

½ cup dried hops
½ cup dried lavender

1 cup dried lemon balm
and lemon verbena
leaves, mixed.

Mix all the dried herbs together and place in a sachet made from thin cotton or butter muslin. Place under the pillow, or pin onto it.
For drying herbs, see *Drying and Storing Herbs*, p. 137.

LAVENDER AND THYME SLEEP PILLOW

1 cup dried lavender
1 cup dried thyme
1 cup dried marjoram,
    leaves and flowers

1 tablespoon orris-root
    powder
1 tablespoon ground
    cinnamon
3 tablespoons dried,
    grated orange peel

Mix all the dried herbs together in an air-tight container.
Add the dried orange peel and ground cinnamon and shake
well.
Sprinkle over the orris-root powder, shaking well. Make
sure that the herbs are covered with the sweet orris-root.
Put into sachets.

MINT AND LEMON BALM SLEEP PILLOW

1 cup dried mint leaves
1 cup dried lemon balm
    leaves
½ cup dried lemon verbena
    leaves

1 cup dried rose petals,
    any fragrant variety
1 teaspoon ground cloves

Put all the herbs into a plastic air-tight container and mix
well.
Sprinkle over the ground cloves, shaking well.
Sew into sachets.

TIPS FOR SLEEP PILLOWS
You can fill sleep pillows with freshly picked herbs, but you will find that the smell is not very strong, and after one or two weeks the pillow will have lost its scent. It is best to use dry herbs, as the aroma lasts longer. When the pillow is losing its scent, shake the mixture around inside and add a few drops of essential oil to the mixture, to revive the fragrance.

If you sleep on your right side, pin or sew the sleep pillow onto the right side, so that when you are asleep you will inhale the smell directly.

It is an old superstition to burn the sleep pillow after one full week of sleep. By doing so you are cured, so you have no more need for the pillow. It is also said that if you sleep with your head pointing north, the earth's currents will send magical soothing rhythms to put you to sleep.

Tips to Aid Sleep

Make a clear division between day-time and night-time activities before going to bed. Focus your mind away from the stress and tension if you have had an active day.

Before going to bed, first unwind your body and mind. Do things that you enjoy, such as being with friends, reading, knitting or sewing. Go for a walk: the fresh night air will make you feel tired. Then take a warm bath. Sit or lie in a comfortable position, with the lights dim, and listen to soft relaxing music.

Getting too hot at night can be very uncomfortable for you, and unpleasant for your partner. To stay cool:
1) Wear a thin cotton nightie or pyjamas. This is often cooler than sleeping naked.

2) Nylon sheets and brushed cotton can cause you to sweat. Choose a cooler combination such as 60 per cent cotton, to 40 per cent polyester.

3) Dust yourself well with talc after your bath.

4) It is better to have the bedroom too cold than too hot while you are sleeping. Keep the room temperature at about 64°–66°F (19C–20C).

5) A sweet-smelling, heady, perfumed bed will help you to drop off to sleep, as well as keep you fresh and fragrant throughout the night. Pin a scented sleep pillow to your bed pillow, or put it in or under it.

6) Sprinkle a few drops of oil of lavender onto your nightie, or spray your pillow with a strong, heavy perfume.

7) Make a scented ball using your favourite perfume. Soak a cotton wool pad in the perfume, place it in the middle of a square of cotton, wrap the ball in the cotton and tie a piece of ribbon around to keep it in place. Put this into your pillow case.

MASSAGE

Massaging the feet and hands can also help to induce sleep.

Gently stroke the feet and hands with a soft brush, then, using one of the following, massage with the finger tips using semi-circular movements:

1) warm olive oil
2) sweet almond oil
3) a mixture made up of:
   yolk of 1 fresh egg
   1 tablespoon fuller's earth
   1 tablespoon almond oil

Beat up the egg yolk.

Add the sweet almond oil. Add the earth a little at a time, stirring well.

Massage the hands and feet well, then wash off with warm water. Massage the hands and feet with a little vaseline.

Tips for snoring

1)   Remove anything that might be irritating you or your partner, causing either one of you to snore, such as wool blankets, feather pillows or animal hair.

2)   Lying flat on your back will cause snoring. Have an extra pillow to prop you up a bit. If you are used to sleeping flat you will find an extra pillow uncomfortable and so turn over onto your side.

3)   Don't sleep with your mouth open, as this is likely to cause you to snore. If your partner is the culprit, then gently close his or her lips together.

4)   If you or your partner smoke, try to keep the bedroom free from smoke. Leave the window slightly open or have an air freshener, and don't leave the ashtray beside the bed.

5)   Put some pot plants and flowers in the room or have a jug of fresh water standing beside the bed, so that there is enough humidity as snoring is mostly caused by dry nasal membranes.

6)   This may sound a little cruel, but it works. When your partner is snoring, sprinkle a little black pepper onto his or her pillow. This will cause him to sneeze, and so clear the nose and stop the snoring.

5 *Growing your own*

GROWING HERBS IN CONFINED SPACES

Most herbs are available dried. They can be bought from supermarkets, health shops and garden centres, or by mail order. I give a list of suppliers at the back of the book. However, it is a delight to pick and use your own herbs fresh from the garden, and although not everyone who wishes to grow herbs has a garden, there are many herbs that you can grow in pots, tubs, troughs and windowboxes.

These herbs grow well in confined spaces:

Troughs balm, borage, catmint, chamomile, chives, lemon balm, 'Corsican Blue' rosemary, all kinds of thyme and rooted cuttings of bay.

Tubs bay, lemon verbena, marjoram, 'Dwarf Green Curled' parsley and tarragon.

Window Boxes 'Dark Opal' basil, chives, corn salad, cotton lavender, parsley, thymes such as 'Silver Posie', lemon thyme and thyme *thymus erectus*, which grows like a tiny tree.

Indoors in plant pots or tubs, use potting compost: lemon

verbena, mint, 'Dwarf Green' parsley, pineapple, sage, 'Corsican Blue' rosemary.
In Walls catmint, chamomile, curry plant, horehound, marjoram and nasturtium.

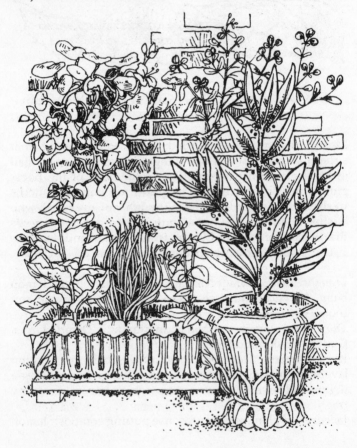

DRYING AND STORING HERBS

During the growing season herbs can be enjoyed fresh. It is delightful to see the beautiful colours and smell the sweet perfume of herbs such as lavender and rosemary, heavy with flowers and buzzing with bees.

Drying herbs is most important, whether they are to be used to make pot-pourri, perfume or cosmetics, or to be used in cooking. Much of the value of the herb can be lost in a matter of hours, if the drying process is hurried, or inefficiently carried out.

Before the herbs are dried, they first must be harvested. Evergreens such as sage, mint, rosemary and thyme can be collected to dry in the winter, as well as the summer. Pick leaves just before the flower becomes fully opened. Unless the herb grows profusely, gather the leaves in small quantities throughout the season. Unearth roots when the top of the herb is beginning to die down. When drying herbs, there are 10 rules that should always be kept in mind and carried out:

1) Herbs should always be gathered on a dry fine day, when there is no dew on the plants.
2) Handle them gently and as little as possible, so not to bruise the leaves.
3) Only gather as many as you can dry at one time. If left to go limp and then dried later, they will be of no use.
4) Never pick any leaf or flower that is marked or damaged in any way.

5)   Never take too much from a herb: only take what you need. No more than one third should be taken from perennial plants. Annuals are different, as they will not come up in the next season. Once the harvesting is done, they should be cut down to the ground or removed completely.

6)   Only ever take from the herb the part that you need: the flowers, leaves or branches.

7)   When you are drying herbs, keep them out of sunlight, as it will destroy their scent and their flavour if they are to be used in cooking.

8)   Different herbs should not be dried together in the same confined space.

9)   Dry the herbs in a warm, dry, airy place. Any moisture will cause mould. Whilst drying they should be turned every 8 hours, to keep the air circulating.

10)   When drying the leaves off the stalk, turn each one every 24 hours.

Once the herbs have been harvested, start the drying process as soon as possible. There are many different methods of drying herbs. Some take more time than others, but all work equally well.

Evergreens such as nettles, mint, sage, rosemary, basil and thyme can be dried in two ways. The best is to pick in a bunch, tie the ends of the stalks and hang them up from rafters, across a dry warm room. Leave for a few days until they are dry, then remove the leaves from the stalks and store in a glass screw-topped jar or an air-tight plastic container.

Label all the herbs well and store in a dark cupboard.

Make sure that the lids are screwed on tight, so that the container cannot re-absorb moisture from the atmosphere. Never use a tin to store herbs as they will sweat and encourage the formation of mould.

Or, spread leaves onto a tray that is lined with muslin, tissue or newspaper stretched between two wooden frames and dry for 2 to 3 days in a warm room or an airy attic: any place where there is a free circulation of air, and always away from direct sunlight.

Be careful not to over-dry herbs, as this will destroy the natural essential oils in the plant. The whole process of drying usually takes about 5 to 6 days. Dryness can be judged by breaking a stem with your fingers: if it is crispy, then the herb is dry and ready to store. Leaves should be crisp enough to crush with your fingers.

Other methods of drying are: spreading the leaves and flowers on a sheet of paper on the floor in a warm room and turning each leaf and flower daily; or, lining a shallow cardboard box with paper, spreading over the leaves or flowers and storing the box in an airing cupboard. An empty greenhouse, or a section of the greenhouse screened off by a plastic sheet hung temporarily to partition, will provide an ideal drying place. Open wooden boxes lined with paper and stacked on top of one another will also provide a good place to dry leaves. Turn the leaves daily, and every few days rearrange the boxes, so that the air is circulating.

Drying herbs in the microwave is a very slow process, but, unlike other methods of drying, the leaves, and especially the flowers, will dry in perfect condition, and the leaves will stay flat. To dry using this method, first line the microwave dish with kitchen paper and place a small cup of water in the middle of the dish. Place the herbs around the cup of water and dry for 5 minutes. Turn each leaf over. Repeat the process several times until the herbs are dried.

There are many different ways of storing the herbs. Remember not to mix different herbs together. Use any container that is air-tight. I have found that a shop sweet jar is the best: ask your friendly shopkeeper to save them for you when they are empty. Glass screw-topped jars are also very useful for storing. Leaves can be stored in jars, or put into paper bags and placed in clean empty wooden drawers, or into sealed cardboard boxes that are then put in the attic, a warm spare room or a warm airing cupboard. Make sure that the containers are washed clean and dried before putting the herbs into them, and label them well.

The most recent way to store herbs is to freeze them. There are three ways to freeze herbs: the first being to cut the sprigs of the herb that you are going to freeze when dry, wash them free of grit and blanche by bringing a large pan of water to the boil, allowing the water to boil deeply for a few minutes and then adding the herb. This is best done by putting the herbs into a sieve or shaker and immersing them in the boiling water. Do this a few times, then put into a container and straight into the freezer. Label the herb, and the date of freezing.

The second method is to freeze the herbs when they are fresh, to use in cooking. Wash the herb under cold water, shake off the drips, then strip the leaves from the stalk. Put them into the freezer on a tray. Leave until firm, then put into freezer bags and back into the freezer. When taken out of the freezer for use, small pieces can be broken off and used in salads.

The third way is very quick and simple. Chop the herbs very finely, mix with water and freeze in blocks. This method is suitable to use in soups, sauces, and gravies.

Whatever method you use for freezing herbs, the first four rules for drying herbs must be followed when harvesting.

6   Herb lore and legend

During the background reading for this book, I have learnt a lot about herb lore, history and legend.

In the beginning of the 18th century, physicians were seen travelling around the English countryside, collecting and preparing wild herbs such as mint and thyme. They are remembered today in the names of country pubs and inns, such as 'The Myrtle Tree Inn', and 'The Green Man'. The sign of the 'Green Man' refers to the collectors of herbs, who used to distil the volatile oils from the herbs. An inn would have been the ideal place to set up a still, which accounts for the name 'Green Man Still'.

Some say the green man is also Jack-in-the-Green, a young chimney-sweep who used to dress in green leaves and boughs as he led the May Day processions and danced through the streets. Another suggestion is that the 'Green Man' is the figure of Robin Hood in his coat of Lincoln green.

Herbs have always been connected with witchcraft. According to Greek mythology, it was the Greek goddess Hecate who first taught magic, sorcery and witchcraft. Then Hecate taught her two daughters Medea and Circe the properties of herbs. This proved invaluable in the education of witches: not only black witches, but also the half-grey and white witches that work only for good. The deadly nightshade, mint, aconite, azalea and osiers were all dedicated to Hecate, as were the mandrake and cyclamen.

During the 16th century hundreds of poor, old skinny 'hags' were tied up and put into sacks, then thrown into deep rivers to prove their innocence. If they swam or floated to the river's surface then they were witches, and would be dragged from the river and either burnt in the market place or sent to the hanging tree. If they drowned, they were innocent and their name would be cleared. What was left was buried in unhallowed ground. An aspen was then laid on the grave to prevent her from riding abroad. The superstitions that are connected with herbs are both intriguing and fascinating, and the list of witchcraft plants is long.

A cracked old Yew tree is said to have stood in the corner of the witch's garden, but although yew wood was used for making bows for archers, the wood was unsuitable for broomsticks, so the witch had to depend on the ash tree. When used for a broom-handle, the ash wood would protect her from drowning. The broom bristles were made from birch twigs, which were tied together with osiers: The osier is one of the seven plants dedicated to the Greek goddess Hecate who taught magic, therefore it is a protection for witches.

A tall, straggly hawthorn hedge surrounded her property. Witches were believed to seek shelter in hawthorn hedges, and only ever to cross over it at night, to pick herbs.

Ragwort was one of her favourite herbs as, if her broomstick was not at hand, she could change the ragwort into a horse, so that she could fly over the countryside. A bundle of hay would serve if ragwort was not at hand, but she had to work hard on it.

In his portrayal of witches, Ben Jonson shows an intimate knowledge of herbs and their properties.

The Envious say
The venom'd Plants
Wherewith shee Kills; where the sad Mandrake growes,
Those grones are deathfull: the dead-numming
 Nightshade!
The stupifying Hemlock! Adders tongue! and Martagon!
Our hearts pound, our skin crawls and we shudder
 happily.
(*from 'The Sad Shepherd'*)

Deadly Nightshade (*Atropa bella-donna*)

According to Greek mythology, there were three fates: the first was Clotho, who held the distaff; Lachesis spun the thread of life and Atropos cut the thread when life was ended. The deadly nightshade was named after Atropos.

Elder (*Samucus nigra*)

There are many legends connected with the elder. One of them is that in the elder tree branches dwells Hyldle-Moer, the elder tree's mother, who lives inside the tree and watches over it. Should the tree be cut down and furniture made of the wood, Hyldle-Moer will follow her property and haunt the owners until death. In Denmark they believe that if you stand under an elder tree on Midsummer's Eve, you will see the King of Fairyland ride by. It is also not considered wise to sleep under the elder: perhaps the vision of the King would result in drugging you to sleep. It was an old Gloucestershire custom to trim an elder bush into the shape of a cross and plant it on a newly-dug grave. If the bush blossomed the next year, the soul of the person beneath was happy.

Fennel (Sow or Hog's) (Peucedanum officinale)
Fennel is one of many anti-witch herbs. When in the house it will protect the owners from all evil. In medieval times, fennel was employed, together with St John's wort, as a preventative of witchcraft, being hung over doors on Midsummer's Eve to warn off evil spirits. It will cure infection in the eyes, in animals as well as humans, and many swear by fennel tea, saying that it will absorb poisons in the body.

Hyssop (Hyssopus officinalis)
Hyssop is the holy herb, because it was used for cleaning sacred places. In the scriptures it says, 'Purge me with hyssop, and I shall be clean!' In the Holy Land, six different species of hyssop are grown. When Jesus was on the cross, one disciple filled a sponge with vinegar, and put hyssop upon it and put it to his mouth. After he had received the drink he said, 'It is finished.' Then he bowed his head and gave up the ghost.

Juniper (Juniperus communis)
In Italy, branches of juniper are hung over doors to protect from enchantment and to ward off witches. It is an old custom in France to burn juniper and rosemary together in hospitals, to purify the air and protect from infection. The bitter oil of wormwood is used in absinthe, and the berries of some species of juniper are a component of gin. Juniper represents asylum, protection.

Lemon balm (*Melissa officinalis*)

Nothing but good can be said about this herb. Bees are delighted with this herb above all others. It acts as a signpost for any bee that is in danger of getting lost: it will follow the scent, and always find its way home. Lemon balm leaves are still rubbed inside the hive today, to encourage any new swarm to stay.

John Hussey of Sydenham lived to be 116 years old, which he attributed to taking a cup of lemon balm tea sweetened with honey daily. The Prince of Glamorgan who lived to be 108 years old also drank the tea daily. The plant is said to be a safeguard against early senility and impotency. Lemon balm was the favoured herb of the great medieval herbalist Paracelsus, who sold the remedy to kings as an elixir of life.

Marjoram (*Origanum vulgare*)

The name *Origanum* comes from the Greek word, *Oros* (mountain) and *ganos* (joy).

Gerard said, 'The leaves boiled in water, and the decoction drunke, easeth such as are given to overmuch sighing.'

The Knight of The Burning Pestle makes plain the dependence of the bear on marjoram:

Where the bee can suck no honey, she leaves her sting behind,

and where the bear cannot find origanum to heal his grief,

he blasteth all over the leaves with his breath.

(*from the prologue of 'The Knight of The Burning Pestle' by Sir Francis Beaumont.*)

It is said that German witches hate marjoram, as it protects against their evil spells and will also drive away ghosts and goblins. To the Greeks, if marjoram grew on a new grave, the soul of the person beneath departed from this world happy. It was an old custom amongst the Greeks and Romans to crown young couples with marjoram. Marjoram and wild thyme laid down by milk in a dairy will prevent it being turned by thunder.

Rosemary (Rosmarinus officinalis)

Rosemary has a reputation for strengthening the memory, especially for lovers. It is used to decorate the church at weddings, and as incense, both in religious ceremonies and in carrying out magical spells. At weddings it was dipped in holy water and entwined in the bride's head-dress. Anne of Cleves wore such a wreath at her wedding. A rosemary branch, tied with ribbons of all colours, was presented to the wedding guests.

Sicilians believe that young fairies, taking the form of snakes, lie amongst the branches of the rosemary bush. It is still a custom today in Wales to carry a sprig of rosemary and to cast it onto the coffin as it is being lowered into the grave. In Gloucestershire, it is believed that rosemary will not grow unless the mistress is the master in her house.

Rosemary brings love, and will open the hearts of all men.

Let this Rosemary, this flower of men, be a sign of your wisdom, love, and loyalty, be carried not only in the hand, but also in the heart.

Witch hazel (Hamamelis virginiana)

Witch hazel was chosen by the Saxons for their temples, the

hazel being one of Thor's trees. The first Christian church in England was built in Glastonbury of wattles of hazel. In Sweden, oats that are fed to horses are first touched with a hazel bough as a protection against the evil eye. It is also believed in Sweden that he who eats the hazel nuts will become invisible, and the nuts are used for divination on Nutcrack Night, on All Hallow's Eve.

A forked twig of hazel was made into a divining-rod, as it had the power to seek out witches. It was used in water divining, and also to detect buried treasure. It was with a hazel bough that St Patrick drove the snakes out of Ireland. All folklorists agree about the magic and protective virtues of the tree. In Germany the hazel tree is known as *Zauber-Straunch*, which means The Magic Tree.

7 Suppliers

Borchelt Herb Gardens
474 Carriage Shop Road
East Falmouth Mass 02536,
USA.

Chalk Farm Nutrition Centre
Chalk Farm Road
London, NW1.

Culpeper Ltd
Hadstock Road
Linton
Cambridge CB1 6NJ.
(Mail order customers only)

John Bell & Croydon
Wigmore Street
London, W1.
(Cosmetics)

Meadowbrook Herb Garden
Route 138
Wyoming, R1 02898, USA.

Rocky Hollow Herb Farm
Box 354
Sussex,
NJ 07461, USA.

Robert Jackson ltd
170 Piccadilly
London, W1.

Robert Tisserand
Aromatic Oil Co
12 Littlegate Street
Oxford, Oxon.

The Tool Shed Herb Farm
Salem Center
Purd's Station
NY 10578, USA.